Abacus evolve

Photocopy Masters

Ginn

Contents

The Photocopy Masters are of three levels of difficulty: ● support ●● core ●●● enrichment and extension

Unit name	⦿	⦿⦿	⦿⦿⦿
C3 Handling data		104, 174a, 174b	104, 174b
C3 Measures	105	105, 106, 175a, 175b	106, 175a, 175b
C3 Shape and space	107	107, 176a	176a, 176b
D3 Shape and space	108, 109, 177a, 177b, 178a	108, 109, 110, 177a, 177b, 178a, 178b	110, 178b
D3 Calculations	111, 112, 179a, 180a	112, 113, 179b, 180a	113, 180b
E3 Fractions, decimals and percentages, ratio and proportion	114, 117, 118, 181a, 182a	114, 115, 116, 117, 118, 181b	116, 181b, 182b
E3 Properties of numbers and number sequences; Solving problems	183a	119, 120, 183b	119, 120
E3 Properties of numbers and number sequences	121, 184a	121, 122, 123, 184b	122, 123, 184b

Resource sheets	
185	Circles with 10 divisions
186	Circles with 8 divisions
187	Circles with 6 divisions
188	Fraction cards
189	Fraction board
190	Fraction lines
191	Tenths and hundredths grids
192	Kittens bar line graph
193	Kittens frequency table
194	Rainy days in Devon bar line graph
195	Rainy days in Spain bar line graph
196	Sunny days in England frequency table
197	Sunny days in Scotland frequency table
198	Tea temperature line graphs
199	Noise level line graph
200	January temperatures line graph
201	Ice cube line graph
202	12 times table line graph
203	Blank line graph
204	Blank Carroll diagram
205	Blank Venn diagram
206	Place-value grid 1
207	Place-value grid 2
208	Place-value grid 3
209	100-square 1
210	100-square 2
211	Multiplication grid
212	Blank number lines

213	Shape cards 1
214	Shape cards 2
215	Shape cards 3
216	Shape board 1
217	Shape board 2
218	Symmetrical leaves
219	Symmetrical flower
220	Tetrahedron net
221	Cube net
222	Square-based pyramid net
223	Cuboid net
224	Mud houses
225	Distances between cities
226	Round trips
227	Recipes
228	Days in a month
229	Types of clock
230	Train timetables
231	Ship and flight timetables
232	Cinema timetables
233	Blank analogue clocks
234	Blank digital clocks
235	Temperatures around the world
236	Coordinates board
237	Probability cards
238	Football league table
239	Animal water requirements
240	Angles board
241	Right angles
242	Squared paper
243	Square dotted paper
244	Isometric dotted paper
245	Distances in Britain mileage chart

Assessment sheets	
PCM A	Assessment 1
PCM B	Assessment 2
PCM C	Assessment 3
PCM D	Assessment 4
PCM E	Assessment 5
PCM F	Assessment 6
PCM G	Assessment 7
PCM H	Assessment 8
PCM I	Assessment 9
PCM J	Assessment 10
PCM K	Assessment 11
PCM L	Assessment 12
PCM M	Assessment 13

Name _____

Abacus Evolve Framework Edition Year 5 PCM © Harcourt Education Ltd 2007

4-digit numbers

A game for two players, one using the top half of this sheet, the other using the bottom half.
Shuffle a set of 0–9 number cards and place them in a pile, face down. Take turns to turn over a card. Try to write the number in one of your boxes to match the number written below it. If you can't, you must write it in one of your opponent's boxes, if possible. The winner is the first to have all their three numbers completed.

Player A

three thousand, six hundred and twenty-nine

two thousand, eight hundred and seven

five thousand, four hundred and eighteen

Player B

four thousand, seven hundred and thirty-two

one thousand, eight hundred and fifty-nine

seven thousand and sixty-four

PS

5-digit numbers

A game for two players, one using the top half of this sheet, the other using the bottom half.
Shuffle a set of 0–9 number cards and place them in a pile, face down. Take turns to turn over a card. Try to write the number in one of your boxes to match the number written below it. If you can't, you must write it in one of your opponent's boxes, if possible. The winner is the first to have all their three numbers completed.

Player A

eighteen thousand, seven hundred and forty-two

twenty thousand, six hundred and eighty-nine

forty-three thousand, five hundred and six

Player B

fifty-two thousand, three hundred and eighty-six

sixty-one thousand and ninety-four

ninety thousand, seven hundred and fifty-two

PS

Name ....

Abacus Evolve Framework Edition Year 5 PCM © Harcourt Education Ltd 2007

Digit values

Write the value of the digit 4 in each number.

1. 1473   ⟹   .... 4 hundreds ....

2. 274   ⟹   ....

3. 13642   ⟹   ....

4. 24751   ⟹   ....

5. 43073   ⟹   ....

6. 164382   ⟹   ....

Now write the value of the digit 8 in each of these numbers.

7. 3816   ⟹   ....

8. 23082   ⟹   ....

9. 58614   ⟹   ....

10. 84329   ⟹   ....

11. 7628   ⟹   ....

12. 871043   ⟹   ....

PS

Name ....

Multiplication facts

Complete the multiplications.

1. $4 \times 5 =$ ....

2. $3 \times 7 =$ ....

3. $3 \times 9 =$ ....

4. $6 \times 5 =$ ....

5. $5 \times 8 =$ ....

6. $7 \times 6 =$ ....

7. $9 \times 7 =$ ....

8. $4 \times 4 =$ ....

9. $6 \times 6 =$ ....

10. $7 \times 5 =$ ....

11. $8 \times 4 =$ ....

12. $6 \times 8 =$ ....

13. $9 \times 6 =$ ....

14. $4 \times 9 =$ ....

15. $5 \times 9 =$ ....

16. $7 \times 7 =$ ....

17. $4 \times 7 =$ ....

18. $9 \times 9 =$ ....

19. $7 \times 8 =$ ....

20. $8 \times 8 =$ ....

PS

Name _____

Division facts

Complete the divisions.

1. $42 \div 7 =$ _____

2. $27 \div 3 =$ _____

3. $35 \div 5 =$ _____

4. $63 \div 9 =$ _____

5. $28 \div 7 =$ _____

6. $24 \div 8 =$ _____

7. $40 \div 8 =$ _____

8. $20 \div 5 =$ _____

9. $54 \div 9 =$ _____

10. $21 \div 3 =$ _____

11. $36 \div 4 =$ _____

12. $56 \div 8 =$ _____

13. $18 \div 3 =$ _____

14. $81 \div 9 =$ _____

15. $72 \div 8 =$ _____

16. $56 \div 7 =$ _____

17. $45 \div 5 =$ _____

18. $24 \div 4 =$ _____

19. $32 \div 4 =$ _____

20. $49 \div 7 =$ _____

PS

Multiplication and division

Complete each set of calculations.

1. $4 \times 8 =$ ....
    $40 \times 8 =$ ....
    $3200 \div 40 =$ ....
    $320 \div 8 =$ ....

2. $7 \times 6 =$ ....
    $70 \times 60 =$ ....
    $4200 \div 70 =$ ....
    $420 \div 6 =$ ....

3. $8 \times 8 =$ ....
    $80 \times 8 =$ ....
    $6400 \div 80 =$ ....
    $640 \div 80 =$ ....

4. $5 \times 10 =$ ....
    $500 \times 10 =$ ....
    $5000 \div 50 =$ ....
    $500 \div 10 =$ ....

5. $3 \times 12 =$ ....
    $30 \times 120 =$ ....
    $3600 \div 30 =$ ....
    $36\,000 \div 120 =$ ....

6. $3 \times 9 =$ ....
    $90 \times 3 =$ ....
    $2700 \div 90 =$ ....
    $270 \div 3 =$ ....

7. $4 \times 11 =$ ....
    $40 \times 110 =$ ....
    $4400 \div 40 =$ ....
    $440 \div 11 =$ ....

8. $6 \times 3 =$ ....
    $60 \times 30 =$ ....
    $18\,000 \div 30 =$ ....
    $180 \div 6 =$ ....

Solve these problems

9. Padma read 120 pages of her book in 30 days. How many pages did she read a day? Use the quickest method you can to solve this. ....

10. Simon was starting a marble selling business. He had 720 marbles and put them in bags of 8 marbles. How many bags will he have at the end? ....

11. Sheema saved £20 a week for 70 weeks. How much had she accumulated at the end of this time? ....

PS

Name _____

Abacus Evolve Framework Edition Year 5 PCM © Harcourt Education Ltd 2007

Remainder patterns

Divide each number in the multiplication square by 5.

1	2	3	4	5	6	7	8	9	10
2	4	6	8	10	12	14	16	18	20
3	6	9	12	15	18	21	24	27	30
4	8	12	16	20	24	28	32	36	40
5	10	15	20	25	30	35	40	45	50
6	12	18	24	30	36	42	48	54	60
7	14	21	28	35	42	49	56	63	70
8	16	24	32	40	48	56	64	72	80
9	18	27	36	45	54	63	72	81	90
10	20	30	40	50	60	70	80	90	100

Write the remainders in the matching squares in this grid.

1	2	3	4	0	1	2	3	4	0

PS

Name ....

Dividing by 10

Write the missing numbers.

1. $80 \div 10 = $ ....

2. $71 \div 10 = $ ....

3. $46 \div 10 = $ ....

4. $\dfrac{93}{10} = $ ....

5. $470 \div 10 = $ ....

6. $526 \div 10 = $ ....

7. .... $\div 10 = 3.4$

8. .... $\div 10 = 2\dfrac{7}{10}$

9. .... $\div 10 = 8\dfrac{1}{10}$

10. .... $\div 10 = 7.3$

11. $\dfrac{19}{10} = $ ....

12. .... $\div 10 = 4\dfrac{9}{10}$

13. $4 \div 10 = $ ....

14. $265 \div 10 = $ ....

15. .... $\div 10 = 43.1$

16. .... $\div 10 = 0.9$

Abacus Evolve Framework Edition Year 5 PCM © Harcourt Education Ltd 2007

PS

Abacus Evolve Framework Edition Year 5 PCM © Harcourt Education Ltd 2007

Odds and evens

Write 'odd' or 'even' for each total.

1. odd + odd + odd = ...

2. even + even + odd + odd = ...

3. odd + even + odd + even + odd = ...

4. odd – odd + even – even = ...

5. even – odd + even – odd = ...

6. odd + odd + even – even = ...

7. 3 odd numbers and 3 even numbers = ...

8. 6 odd numbers and 4 even numbers = ...

9. 5 odd numbers and 3 even numbers = ...

10. 2 odd numbers and 3 even numbers = ...

11. 4 even numbers and 5 odd numbers = ...

Name ....

Sequences

Write the next four numbers in each sequence.

1. | 325 | 350 | 375 | | | | |
|---|---|---|---|---|---|---|

2. | 85 | 80 | 75 | | | | |
|---|---|---|---|---|---|---|

3. | 31 | 36 | 41 | | | | |
|---|---|---|---|---|---|---|

4. | 72 | 67 | 62 | | | | |
|---|---|---|---|---|---|---|

5. | 35 | 50 | 65 | | | | |
|---|---|---|---|---|---|---|

6. | 33 | 44 | 55 | | | | |
|---|---|---|---|---|---|---|

7. | 22 | 29 | 36 | | | | |
|---|---|---|---|---|---|---|

8. | 62 | 56 | 50 | | | | |
|---|---|---|---|---|---|---|

9. | $7\frac{1}{2}$ | 9 | $10\frac{1}{2}$ | | | | |
|---|---|---|---|---|---|---|

10. | 8 | $7\frac{3}{4}$ | $7\frac{1}{2}$ | | | | |
|---|---|---|---|---|---|---|

11. | $8\frac{2}{3}$ | $9\frac{1}{3}$ | 10 | | | | |
|---|---|---|---|---|---|---|

12. | 5·2 | 6·4 | 7·6 | | | | |
|---|---|---|---|---|---|---|

PS

Abacus Evolve Framework Edition Year 5 PCM © Harcourt Education Ltd 2007

Positions

Write the position of each pointer.

1.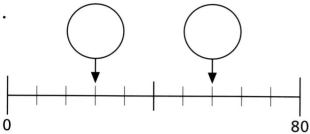

2.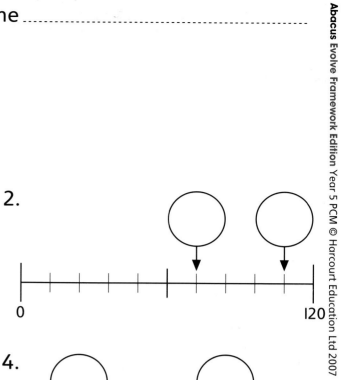

3.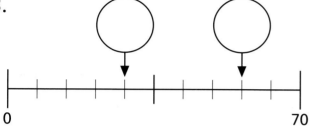

4.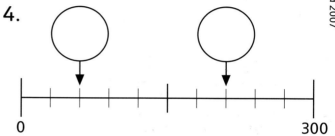

5.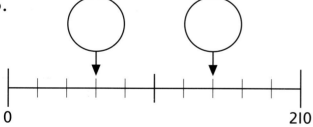

6.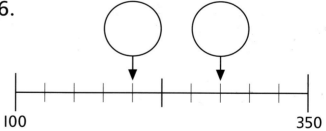

7.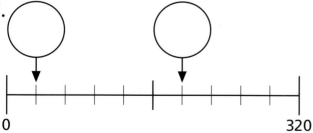

8.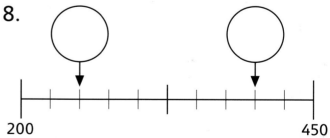

9.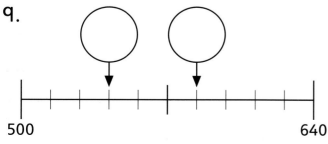

10.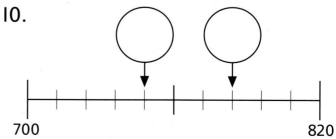

PS

Name ....

Parallel lines

Find pairs of parallel lines on the football pitch.
Use different coloured pencils to show each pair.
The four dots represent footballers. The two pairs create parallel lines.
Draw some more sets of four footballers on the pitch, and join them with parallel lines.

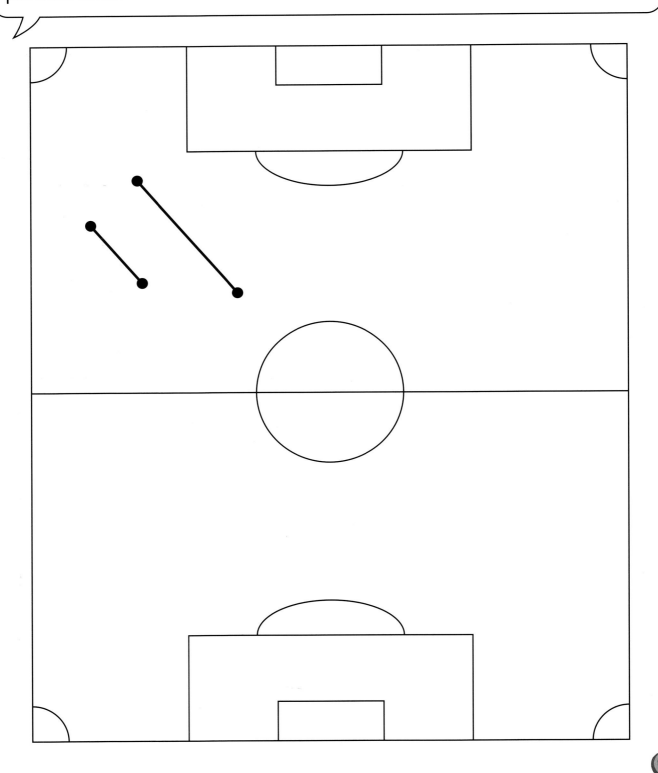

Abacus Evolve Framework Edition Year 5 PCM © Harcourt Education Ltd 2007

Triangles

Colour in a different triangle on each of the grids.
Write the name of each type of triangle.

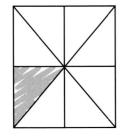 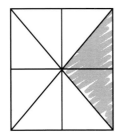 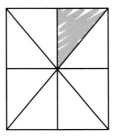 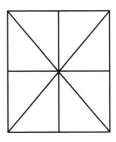

right-angled isosceles right-angled ‑‑‑‑‑‑‑‑‑‑‑‑‑‑‑‑‑‑‑‑‑‑‑

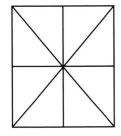 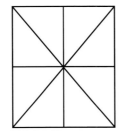 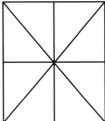 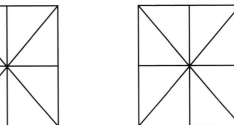

‑‑‑‑‑‑‑‑‑‑‑‑‑‑‑‑‑ ‑‑‑‑‑‑‑‑‑‑‑‑‑‑‑‑‑ ‑‑‑‑‑‑‑‑‑‑‑‑‑‑‑‑‑ ‑‑‑‑‑‑‑‑‑‑‑‑‑‑‑‑‑

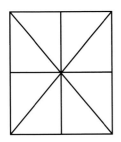 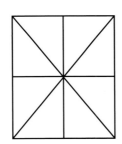 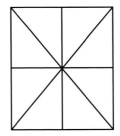 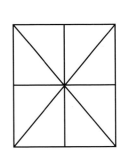

‑‑‑‑‑‑‑‑‑‑‑‑‑‑‑‑‑ ‑‑‑‑‑‑‑‑‑‑‑‑‑‑‑‑‑ ‑‑‑‑‑‑‑‑‑‑‑‑‑‑‑‑‑ ‑‑‑‑‑‑‑‑‑‑‑‑‑‑‑‑‑

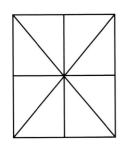 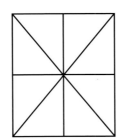 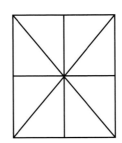 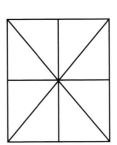

‑‑‑‑‑‑‑‑‑‑‑‑‑‑‑‑‑ ‑‑‑‑‑‑‑‑‑‑‑‑‑‑‑‑‑ ‑‑‑‑‑‑‑‑‑‑‑‑‑‑‑‑‑ ‑‑‑‑‑‑‑‑‑‑‑‑‑‑‑‑‑

PS

Name

Triangles

A
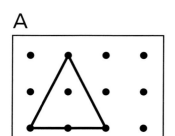

B
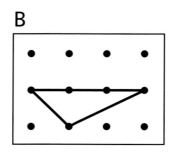

C
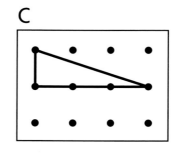

D
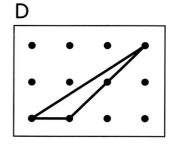

E
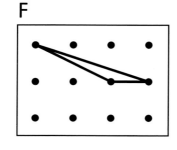

F
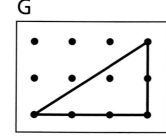

G
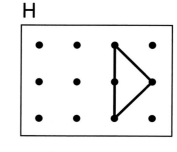

H

I

J
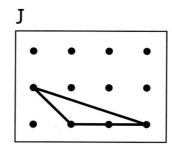

K
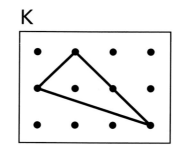

L
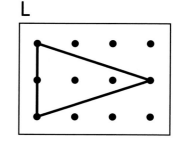

M
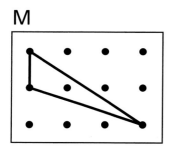

N
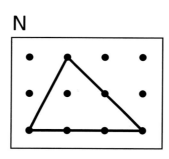

O
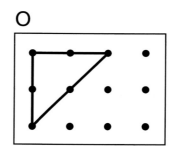

P
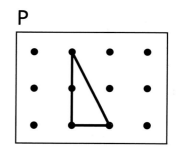

Write the letter of the triangles that belong to each of these types.

right-angled

isosceles

scalene

PS

Abacus Evolve Framework Edition Year 5 PCM © Harcourt Education Ltd 2007

Goals bar line graph

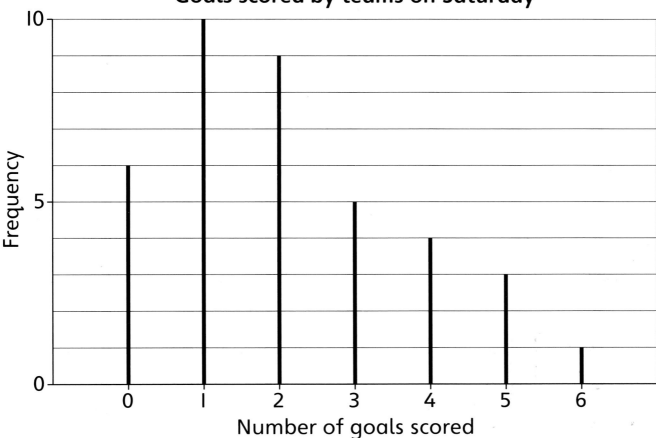

Goals scored by teams on Saturday

How many teams scored:

1. 2 goals? ....

2. 5 goals? ....

3. 1 goal? ....

4. 4 goals? ....

5. 0 goals? ....

6. 3 goals? ....

7. 3 or 4 goals? ....

8. 4 or 5 goals? ....

9. more than 4 goals? ....

10. less than 2 goals? ....

11. an odd number of goals? ....

12. The mode is .... goals.

13. How many goals were scored altogether? ....

PS

Dice bar line graph

These were the scores when a dice was thrown 32 times.

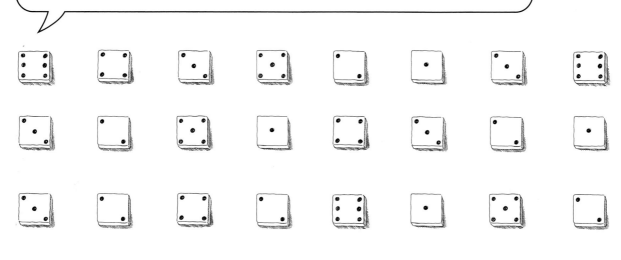

Complete the bar line graph to show the results.

32 throws of a dice

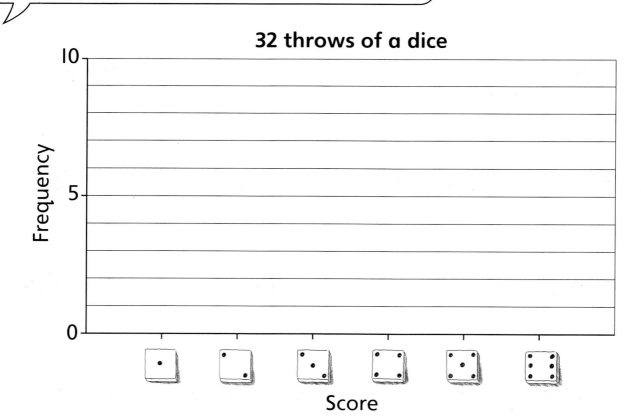

Score

Abacus Evolve Framework Edition Year 5 PCM © Harcourt Education Ltd 2007

Miles and kilometres

Write '<', '>' or '=' between each pair of distances.
Remember: 8 km is about 5 miles.

1. 80 km [ ] 50 miles

2. 10 miles [ ] 12 km

3. 20 km [ ] 15 miles

4. 5 km [ ] 8 miles

5. 24 km [ ] 18 miles

6. 16 km [ ] 10 miles

7. 6 km [ ] 6 miles

8. 10 km [ ] 16 miles

9. 20 miles [ ] 36 km

10. 50 miles [ ] 70 km

11. 32 km [ ] 20 miles

12. 4 km [ ] 2 miles

13. $2\frac{1}{2}$ miles [ ] 6 km

14. 0·8 km [ ] 0·5 miles

15. 100 miles [ ] 150 km

16. 7·5 miles [ ] 12 km

PS

Name ....

Running track

A running track is 200 m start to finish.
Write in metres how far you travel for these numbers of laps.

1. 2 laps = ... m

2. 5 laps = ... m

3. 10 laps = ... m

4. $4\frac{1}{2}$ laps = ... m

5. 8·5 laps = ... m

6. 6·1 laps = ... m

Write in kilometres how far you travel for these numbers of laps.
Use decimals.

7. 7 laps = ... km

8. 11 laps = ... km

9. 4 laps = ... km

10. 8·3 laps = ... km

Write how many laps you run over these distances.
Use mixed numbers.

11. 1 km = ... laps

12. 500 m = ... laps

13. 4·5 km = ... laps

14. 6000 m = ... laps

15. 2·1 km = ... laps

16. 7·3 km = ... laps

PS

Abacus Evolve Framework Edition Year 5 PCM © Harcourt Education Ltd 2007

Name ....

Abacus Evolve Framework Edition Year 5 PCM © Harcourt Education Ltd 2007

Millimetres, centimetres and metres

Complete the pairs of equivalent lengths.

1. 2 cm = ... mm

2. 40 mm = ... cm

3. 30 cm = ... mm

4. .... mm = 1300 cm

5. .... mm = $\frac{1}{4}$ cm

6. 600 cm = ... m

7. $\frac{1}{4}$ m = ... cm

8. 200 mm = ... cm

9. .... m = 350 cm

10. 12 m = ... cm

11. 10 m = ... cm

12. .... m = 2000 mm

13. .... m = 2000 cm

14. .... cm = 25 mm

15. 2·5 m = ... mm

16. .... m = 3500 cm

17. 1·8 cm = ... mm

18. 2·3 m = ... mm

PS

Name ....

Weighing scales

Write each weight in grams.

1.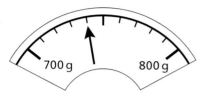

   700 g   800 g

   ------------------ g

2.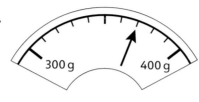

   300 g   400 g

   ------------------ g

3.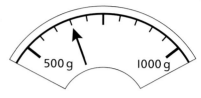

   500 g   1000 g

   ------------------ g

4.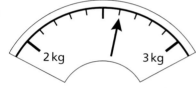

   2 kg   3 kg

   ------------------ g

5.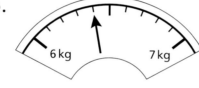

   6 kg   7 kg

   ------------------ g

6.

   1 kg   2 kg

   ------------------ g

7.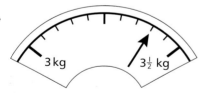

   3 kg $3\frac{1}{2}$ kg

   ------------------ g

8.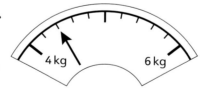

   4 kg   6 kg

   ------------------ g

9.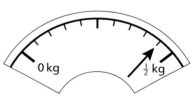

   0 kg $\frac{1}{2}$ kg

   ------------------ g

10.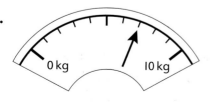

    0 kg   10 kg

    ------------------ g

11.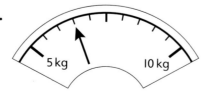

    5 kg   10 kg

    ------------------ g

12.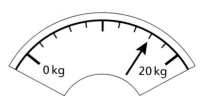

    0 kg   20 kg

    ------------------ g

Abacus Evolve Framework Edition Year 5 PCM © Harcourt Education Ltd 2007

PS

Name ....

Abacus Evolve Framework Edition Year 5 PCM © Harcourt Education Ltd 2007

Grams and kilograms

Complete the pairs of equivalent weights.

1. I kg   = ... g

2. 3000 g = ... kg

3. 10 kg   = ... g

4. 2·5 kg   = ... g

5. 1500 g = ... kg

6. 1·1 kg   = ... g

7. 2300 g = ... kg

8. 4·7 kg   = ... g

9. 0·3 kg   = ... g

10. 7·5 kg   = ... g

11. 800 g   = ... kg

12. 250 g   = ... kg

13. 0·75 kg = ... g

14. 0·01 kg = ... g

PS

Name ....

Axes of symmetry

Draw any axes of symmetry on each shape. Use a ruler!

1.
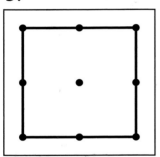

2.
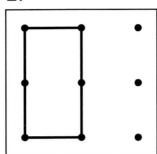

3.
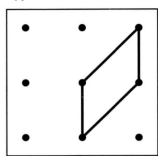

4.
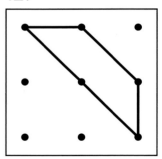

5.
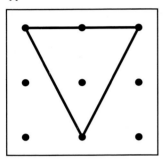

6.
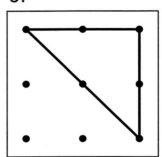

7.
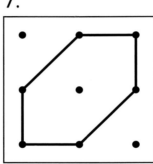

8.
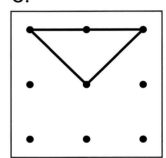

9.
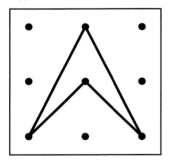

10.
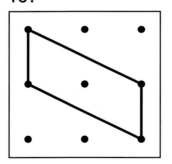

11.
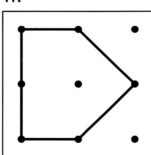

12.
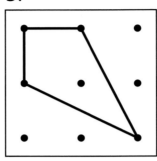

13.
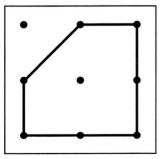

14.
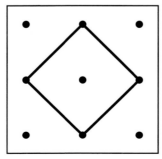

15.
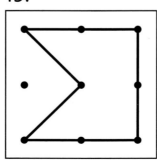

16.
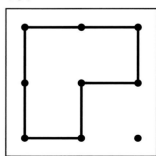

PS

Symmetry game

This is a game for three players.
The first player places a counter on any square on the grid. The second player places another counter on a square that is symmetrical to the first about one of the lines. The third person places two counters on squares that are symmetrical to the first and second counters about the other line of symmetry. Remove the counters and repeat, swapping roles.

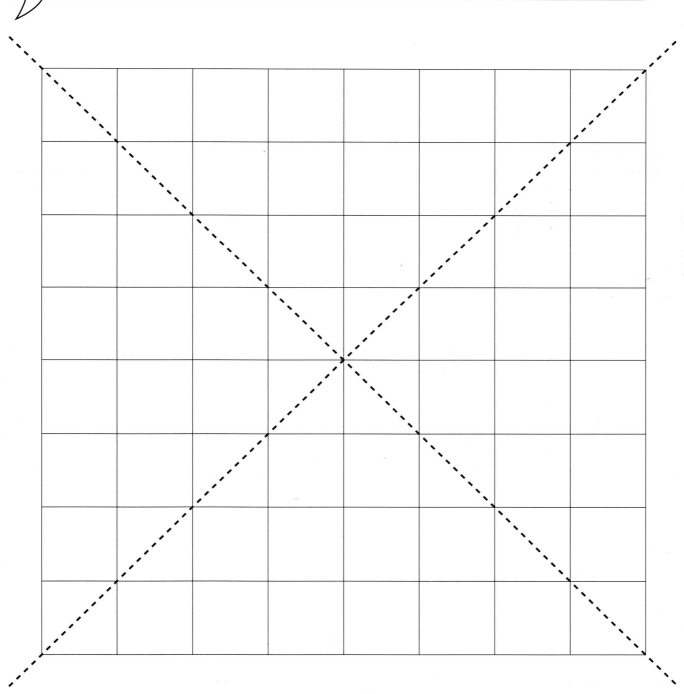

Abacus Evolve Framework Edition Year 5 PCM © Harcourt Education Ltd 2007

PS

Name ....

Symmetrical shapes

Draw a shape on each grid that has reflective symmetry about the dotted line. Try to use as many different shapes as you can.

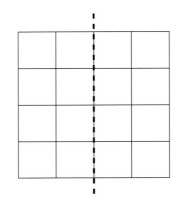
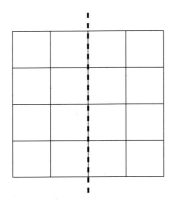
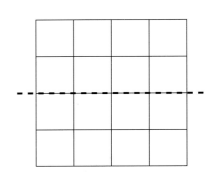

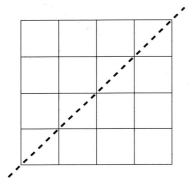
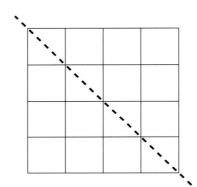
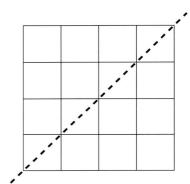

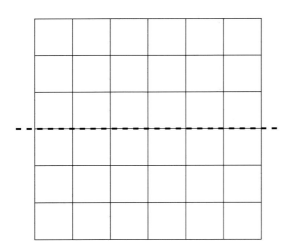
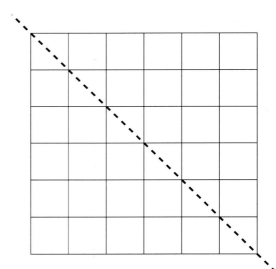

Name

Abacus Evolve Framework Edition Year 5 PCM © Harcourt Education Ltd 2007

Plaiting a tetrahedron

Cut out the net and fold along the lines. Plait by placing 1 over 2, then 3 over 4, lining up the dots. Fold the rest around and tuck 5 underneath 1.

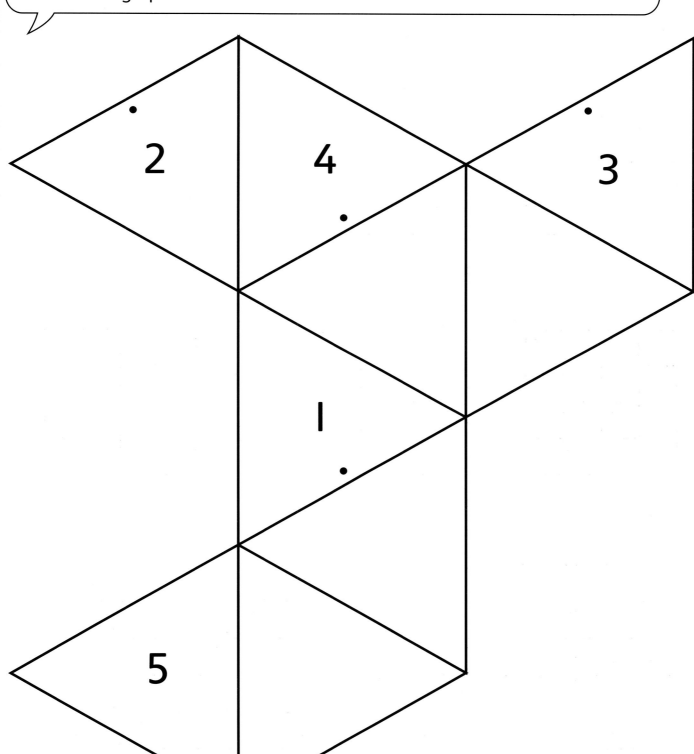

Name ....

Four-cube puzzle

> Draw four equal-sized nets of a cube, like this:

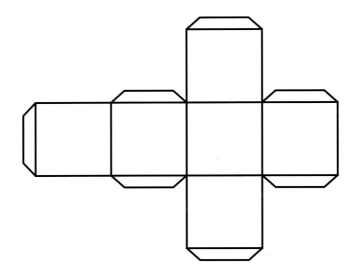

> Colour the nets as shown. (B = blue, G = green, R = red and Y = yellow.)

	R	
R	Y	R
	B	
	G	

	B	
Y	G	G
	R	
	Y	

	G	
B	B	Y
	Y	
	R	

	B	
Y	G	G
	R	
	R	

> Cut out the nets, fold along the lines and glue to make four cubes. Arrange the four cubes to create a cuboid, so that the colours on each face match.

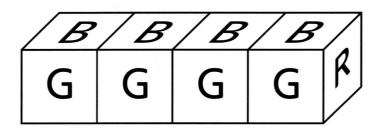

PS

Name _____

Abacus Evolve Framework Edition Year 5 PCM © Harcourt Education Ltd 2007

Pairs to 100

The numbers on each pair of cards total 100.
Write the missing numbers on the blank cards.

1.

2.

3.

4.

5.

6.

7.

8.

9.

10.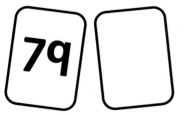

11.

12.

13.

14.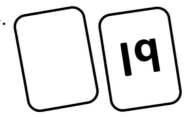

15.

16.

17.

18.

PS

Adding to make 10 and 20

Write the position of each arrow, and then write what needs to be added to it to make 10 (letters A to H) or 20 (I to P).

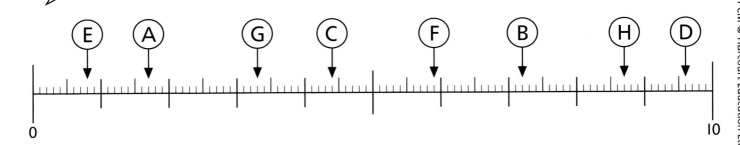

A __1·7__ + __8·3__ = 10   B _____ + _____ = 10

C _____ + _____ = 10   D _____ + _____ = 10

E _____ + _____ = 10   F _____ + _____ = 10

G _____ + _____ = 10   H _____ + _____ = 10

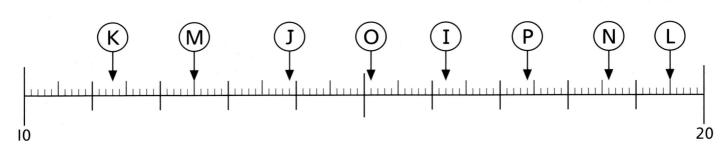

I _____ + _____ = 20   J _____ + _____ = 20

K _____ + _____ = 20   L _____ + _____ = 20

M _____ + _____ = 20   N _____ + _____ = 20

O _____ + _____ = 20   P _____ + _____ = 20

PS

Making the next hundred

This is a game for two players, each with a set of counters in their own colour.
Shuffle a set of 1–100 number cards. Place them face down in a pile.
Take turns to reveal a card. If the number can be added to one of the numbers on the grid to make the next hundred, cover the grid number with one of your counters. Continue taking turns. The winner is the first player to get three counters in a line.

127	585	742	462	356
194	169	118	681	336
270	245	573	187	234
609	358	717	430	623
708	471	814	502	593

Abacus Evolve Framework Edition Year 5 PCM © Harcourt Education Ltd 2007

PS

Name ....

Differences

Write the difference between each pair of numbers.

150   250

1. 214 – 186 = ...

450   550

2. 523 – 479 = ...

750   850

3. 846 – 793 = ...

250   350

4. 317 – 288 = ...

650   750

5. 731 – 674 = ...

850   950

6. 908 – 856 = ...

PS

Name _____

Abacus Evolve Framework Edition Year 5 PCM © Harcourt Education Ltd 2007

Differences

Write the difference between the cost of each pair of holidays.

1.

   FRANCE £187

   Belgium £223

   difference: _____

2.

   MALTA £314

   SPAIN £286

   difference: _____

3.

   ITALY £379

   £421 Greece

   difference: _____

4.

   FLORIDA £469

   NEW YORK £507

   difference: _____

5.

   Oman £619

   DUBAI £576

   difference: _____

6.

   NORWAY £384

   £406 Sweden

   difference: _____

7.

   BRAZIL £864

   CHILE £913

   difference: _____

8.

   JAPAN £821

   HONG KONG £763

   difference: _____

9.

   NEW ZEALAND £1043

   BALI £987

   difference: _____

10.

    Latvia £386

    £427 CROATIA

    difference: _____

11.

    AUSTRIA £286

    Poland £318

    difference: _____

12.

    SICILY £523

    CORSICA £477

    difference: _____

PS

Doubling grids

Complete the doubling grids.

21	95	54
63	32	77
84	46	18

double

42		

38	16	87
67	96	43
59	27	79

double

1·3	3·1	3·8
2·9	2·4	6·2
4·7	6·4	5·6

double

PS

Name

Doubling and halving decimals

Complete the tables.

Abacus Evolve Framework Edition Year 5 PCM © Harcourt Education Ltd 2007

Number	Double
2·4	
8·8	
	8·4
12·6	
	11·2
	13·4
14·4	
1·8	
	22·6
3·4	
	15·4
16·3	

Number	Double
6·2	
3·3	
	11·6
2·7	
15·9	
	17·8
	3·2
13·8	
	9·8
	23·4
17·6	
	15·6

PS

Name ....

Near doubles

Complete the number sentences.

1. double 72 = ...

2. 72 + 75   = ...

3. 68 + 72   = ...

4. 730 + 720 = ...

5. double 46 = ...

6. 49 + 46   = ...

7. 45 + 47   = ...

8. 460 + 480 = ...

9. double 28 = ...

10. 28 + 29   = ...

11. 25 + 28   = ...

12. 260 + 280 = ...

13. double 69 = ...

14. 72 + 69   = ...

15. 69 + 67   = ...

16. 680 + 670 = ...

17. double 57 = ...

18. 55 + 57   = ...

19. 57 + 59   = ...

20. 580 + 550 = ...

21. double 86 = ...

22. 86 + 89   = ...

23. 84 + 86   = ...

24. 870 + 860 = ...

PS

Name

Abacus Evolve Framework Edition Year 5 PCM © Harcourt Education Ltd 2007

Doubles and halves

Work out each double or half, and then mark its position on the number line.

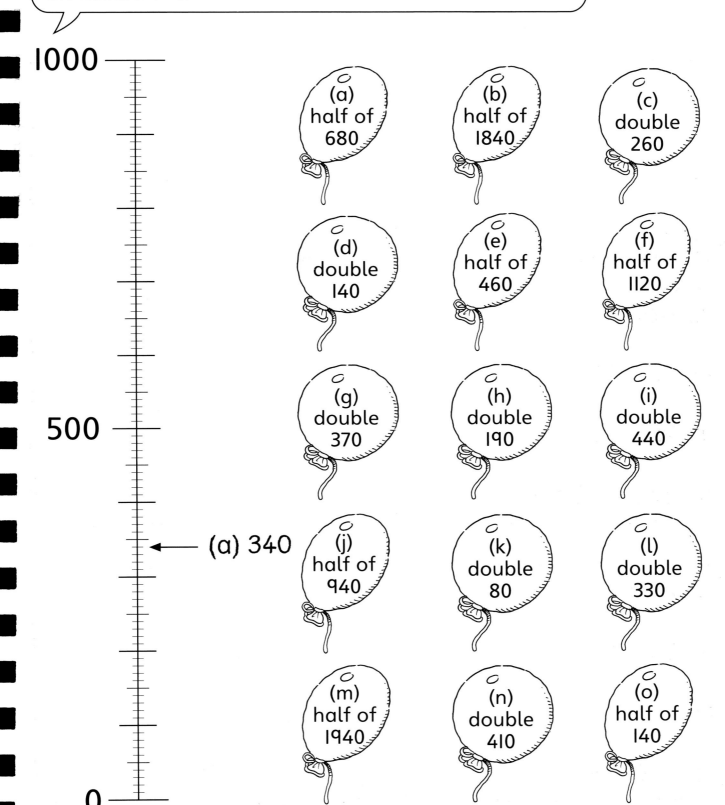

1000

500

(a) 340 ←

0

(a) half of 680

(b) half of 1840

(c) double 260

(d) double 140

(e) half of 460

(f) half of 1120

(g) double 370

(h) double 190

(i) double 440

(j) half of 940

(k) double 80

(l) double 330

(m) half of 1940

(n) double 410

(o) half of 140

PS

Name ....

Ticket prices

> Write the cost of two of each type of ticket.

1. £1·70 ----------------

2. £5·30 ----------------

3. £4·60 ----------------

4. £7·40 ----------------

5. £2·80 ----------------

6. £1·90 ----------------

7. £0·70 ----------------

8. £8·30 ----------------

> Children's tickets are half price.
> Write the cost of each of these tickets for a child.

9. one adult £4·40 ----------------

10. one adult £6·20 ----------------

11. one adult £8·60 ----------------

12. one adult £7·20 ----------------

13. one adult £5·80 ----------------

14. one adult £9·40 ----------------

Abacus Evolve Framework Edition Year 5 PCM © Harcourt Education Ltd 2007

PS

Name _____

Abacus Evolve Framework Edition Year 5 PCM © Harcourt Education Ltd 2007

Mixed numbers

Colour squares in each set to match the mixed number.

1. $3\frac{3}{4}$

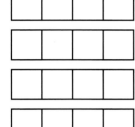

2. $1\frac{3}{5}$

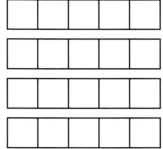

3. $2\frac{5}{6}$

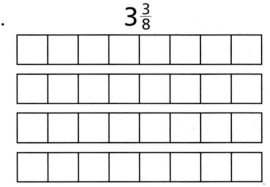

4. $2\frac{2}{3}$

5. $1\frac{5}{7}$

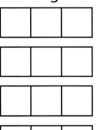

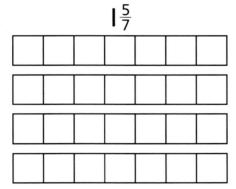

6. $3\frac{3}{8}$

7. $4\frac{9}{10}$

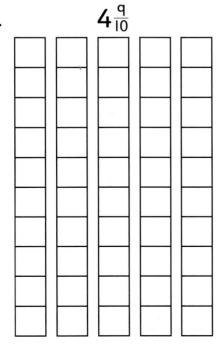

8. $2\frac{7}{9}$

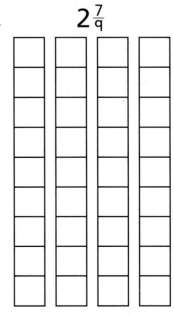

PS

Mixed numbers to improper fractions

Write each mixed number as an improper fraction.

1. $3\frac{1}{4} = \dfrac{\boxed{}}{4}$

2. $2\frac{2}{3} = \dfrac{\boxed{}}{3}$

3. $1\frac{3}{5} = \dfrac{\boxed{}}{5}$

4. $4\frac{2}{7} = \dfrac{\boxed{}}{7}$

5. $7\frac{1}{2} = \dfrac{\boxed{}}{2}$

6. $4\frac{1}{8} = \dfrac{\boxed{}}{8}$

7. $3\frac{7}{10} = \dfrac{\boxed{}}{\boxed{}}$

8. $5\frac{2}{5} = \dfrac{\boxed{}}{\boxed{}}$

9. $2\frac{5}{6} = \dfrac{\boxed{}}{\boxed{}}$

10. $3\frac{3}{8} = \dfrac{\boxed{}}{\boxed{}}$

11. $1\frac{6}{7} = \dfrac{\boxed{}}{\boxed{}}$

12. $4\frac{9}{10} = \dfrac{\boxed{}}{\boxed{}}$

13. $3\frac{2}{9} = \dfrac{\boxed{}}{\boxed{}}$

14. $5\frac{1}{3} = \dfrac{\boxed{}}{\boxed{}}$

15. $7\frac{3}{4} = \dfrac{\boxed{}}{\boxed{}}$

PS

Name _____

Abacus Evolve Framework Edition Year 5 PCM © Harcourt Education Ltd 2007

Improper fractions to mixed numbers

Write each improper fraction as a mixed number.

1. $\dfrac{8}{3}$ =

2. $\dfrac{9}{2}$ =

3. $\dfrac{13}{5}$ =

4. $\dfrac{23}{4}$ =

5. $\dfrac{19}{6}$ =

6. $\dfrac{77}{10}$ =

7. $\dfrac{23}{8}$ =

8. $\dfrac{53}{7}$ =

9. $\dfrac{28}{9}$ =

10. $\dfrac{31}{4}$ =

11. $\dfrac{26}{3}$ =

12. $\dfrac{42}{5}$ =

13. $\dfrac{63}{11}$ =

14. $\dfrac{117}{20}$ =

PS

Name ....

Fractions on a number line

Write the fraction shown by each arrow.

1.

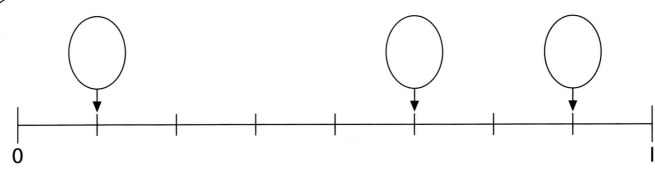

0

2.

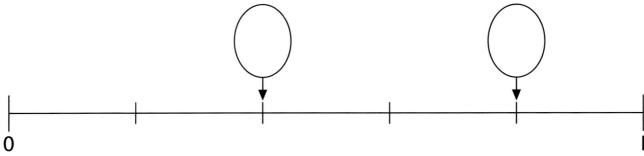

0

3.

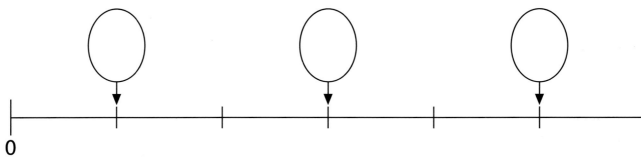

0

4.

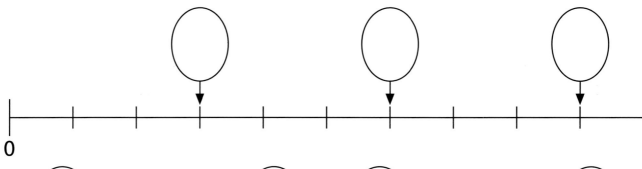

0

5.

0

Abacus Evolve Framework Edition Year 5 PCM © Harcourt Education Ltd 2007

PS

Abacus Evolve Framework Edition Year 5 PCM © Harcourt Education Ltd 2007

Ordering fractions

Write '<', '>' or '=' between each pair of fractions.

1. $\dfrac{3}{4}$ ☐ $\dfrac{5}{8}$

2. $\dfrac{5}{6}$ ☐ $\dfrac{2}{3}$

3. $\dfrac{1}{2}$ ☐ $\dfrac{7}{12}$

4. $\dfrac{11}{12}$ ☐ $\dfrac{5}{6}$

5. $\dfrac{7}{20}$ ☐ $\dfrac{3}{10}$

6. $\dfrac{4}{5}$ ☐ $\dfrac{8}{10}$

7. $\dfrac{11}{20}$ ☐ $\dfrac{3}{5}$

8. $\dfrac{1}{4}$ ☐ $\dfrac{5}{16}$

9. $\dfrac{7}{8}$ ☐ $\dfrac{14}{16}$

10. $\dfrac{2}{3}$ ☐ $\dfrac{7}{12}$

11. $\dfrac{3}{4}$ ☐ $\dfrac{17}{20}$

12. $\dfrac{5}{8}$ ☐ $\dfrac{11}{16}$

13. $\dfrac{3}{4}$ ☐ $\dfrac{2}{3}$

14. $\dfrac{8}{12}$ ☐ $\dfrac{2}{3}$

15. $\dfrac{4}{5}$ ☐ $\dfrac{3}{4}$

16. $\dfrac{3}{8}$ ☐ $\dfrac{5}{6}$

PS

Equivalent fractions

Colour the equivalent fraction on each right-hand grid, and then complete the fractions.

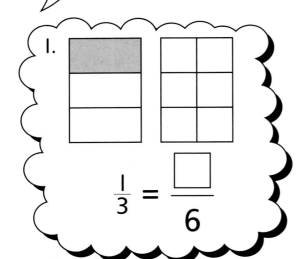

1. $\dfrac{1}{3} = \dfrac{\square}{6}$

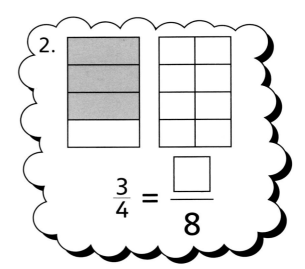

2. $\dfrac{3}{4} = \dfrac{\square}{8}$

3. $\dfrac{\square}{\square} = \dfrac{\square}{\square}$

4. $\dfrac{\square}{\square} = \dfrac{\square}{\square}$

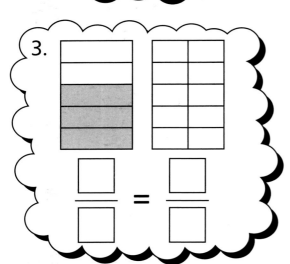

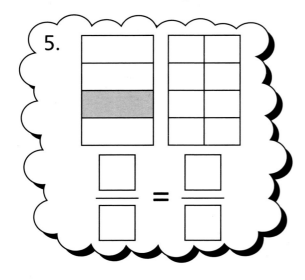

5. $\dfrac{\square}{\square} = \dfrac{\square}{\square}$

6. $\dfrac{\square}{\square} = \dfrac{\square}{\square}$

PS

Name _____

Abacus Evolve Framework Edition Year 5 PCM © Harcourt Education Ltd 2007

Equivalent fractions

Complete each pair of equivalent fractions.

1. $\dfrac{1}{3} = \dfrac{\boxed{}}{6}$

2. $\dfrac{3}{4} = \dfrac{\boxed{}}{8}$

3. $\dfrac{4}{5} = \dfrac{\boxed{}}{10}$

4. $\dfrac{7}{10} = \dfrac{\boxed{}}{20}$

5. $\dfrac{1}{2} = \dfrac{\boxed{}}{6}$

6. $\dfrac{1}{4} = \dfrac{\boxed{}}{12}$

7. $\dfrac{2}{3} = \dfrac{\boxed{}}{9}$

8. $\dfrac{4}{5} = \dfrac{\boxed{}}{10}$

9. $\dfrac{4}{6} = \dfrac{\boxed{}}{3}$

10. $\dfrac{6}{8} = \dfrac{\boxed{}}{4}$

11. $\dfrac{3}{7} = \dfrac{\boxed{}}{35}$

12. $\dfrac{4}{9} = \dfrac{\boxed{}}{27}$

13. $\dfrac{6}{10} = \dfrac{\boxed{}}{20}$

14. $\dfrac{2}{3} = \dfrac{\boxed{}}{21}$

15. $\dfrac{7}{8} = \dfrac{\boxed{}}{40}$

Name ....

Tenths and hundredths

Complete the fractions.

1.
$$\frac{7}{10} = \frac{\boxed{}}{100}$$

2.
$$\frac{90}{100} = \frac{\boxed{}}{10}$$

3.
$$0{\cdot}4 = \frac{\boxed{}}{10}$$

4.
$$0{\cdot}6 = \frac{\boxed{}}{100}$$

5.
$$0{\cdot}8 = \frac{\boxed{}}{5}$$

6.
$$1{\cdot}2 = \frac{\boxed{}}{5}$$

7.
$$0{\cdot}06 = \frac{\boxed{}}{100}$$

8.
$$0{\cdot}04 = \frac{\boxed{}}{25}$$

9.
$$1{\cdot}14 = \frac{\boxed{}}{100}$$

10.
$$1{\cdot}36 = \frac{\boxed{}}{50}$$

11.
$$0{\cdot}25 = \frac{\boxed{}}{4}$$

12.
$$0{\cdot}75 = \frac{\boxed{}}{4}$$

13.
$$0{\cdot}7 = \frac{\boxed{}}{20}$$

14.
$$0{\cdot}35 = \frac{\boxed{}}{20}$$

PS

Name ....

Abacus Evolve Framework Edition Year 5 PCM © Harcourt Education Ltd 2007

Rounding to the nearest thousand and hundred

Round each number of spectators to the nearest thousand and the nearest hundred.

1.
8432
nearest:
thousand ------------------

hundred ------------------

2.
1076
nearest:
thousand ------------------

hundred ------------------

3.
4352
nearest:
thousand ------------------

hundred ------------------

4.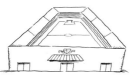
8917
nearest:
thousand ------------------

hundred ------------------

5.
3482
nearest:
thousand ------------------

hundred ------------------

6.
5635
nearest:
thousand ------------------

hundred ------------------

7.
1907
nearest:
thousand ------------------

hundred ------------------

8.
3256
nearest:
thousand ------------------

hundred ------------------

9.
11528
nearest:
thousand ------------------

hundred ------------------

10.
16429
nearest:
thousand ------------------

hundred ------------------

11.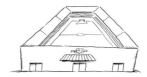
9782
nearest:
thousand ------------------

hundred ------------------

12.
3994
nearest:
thousand ------------------

hundred ------------------

PS

Name _____

Rounding to the nearest hundred

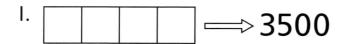

> Use one of each digit to create 4-digit numbers that have the following numbers as their nearest hundred.

1. ⬜⬜⬜⬜ ⟹ 3500

2. ⬜⬜⬜⬜ ⟹ 4800

3. ⬜⬜⬜⬜ ⟹ 7300

4. ⬜⬜⬜⬜ ⟹ 9400

5. ⬜⬜⬜⬜ ⟹ 4400

6. ⬜⬜⬜⬜ ⟹ 3700

7. ⬜⬜⬜⬜ ⟹ 9300

8. ⬜⬜⬜⬜ ⟹ 7400

9. ⬜⬜⬜⬜ ⟹ 7900

10. ⬜⬜⬜⬜ ⟹ 4900

11. ⬜⬜⬜⬜ ⟹ 3800

12. ⬜⬜⬜⬜ ⟹ 9500

13. ⬜⬜⬜⬜ ⟹ 7500

14. ⬜⬜⬜⬜ ⟹ 3900

15. ⬜⬜⬜⬜ ⟹ 5000

16. ⬜⬜⬜⬜ ⟹ 9700

PS

Decimal numbers

Write a decimal number to match each mixed number.

1. three and six tenths

2. fourteen and twenty-eight hundredths

3. fifty-six and three tenths

4. thirty-five and seventy hundredths

5. eighteen and nine hundredths

6. sixty-three hundredths

7. five and eleven hundredths

8. thirteen and eight tenths

9. eighty-eight and eighty-eight hundredths

10. seven and four tenths and three hundredths

11. twenty-seven tenths

12. one hundred and fifty-six hundredths

Abacus Evolve Framework Edition Year 5 PCM © Harcourt Education Ltd 2007

PS

Name ....

Ordering decimals

Write <, > or = between each pair of decimal numbers.

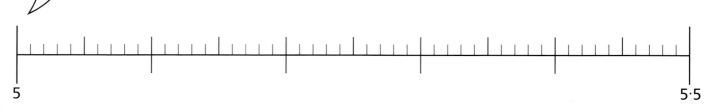

5   5·5

1. 5·4 ☐ 5·3

2. 5·23 ☐ 5·26

3. 5·25 ☐ 5·35

4. 5·35 ☐ 5·53

5. 5·2 ☐ 5

6. 5·25 ☐ 5·5

7. 5·3 ☐ 5·27

8. 5·46 ☐ 5·5

9. 5·29 ☐ 5·3

10. 5·1 ☐ 5·09

11. 5·2 ☐ 5·21

12. 5·34 ☐ 5·43

13. 5·15 ☐ 5·51

14. 5·21 ☐ 5·3

15. $5\frac{3}{10}$ ☐ 5·3

16. $5\frac{17}{100}$ ☐ 5·15

17. 5·2 ☐ $5\frac{21}{100}$

18. 5·35 ☐ $5\frac{3}{10}$

19. 5·4 ☐ $5\frac{39}{100}$

20. 5·06 ☐ $5\frac{1}{10}$

PS

Name ....

Multiplying by 10 and 100

Abacus Evolve Framework Edition Year 5 PCM © Harcourt Education Ltd 2007

Write how many 10p coins are needed to buy each item.

1.

£45

2.

£28

3.

£310

4.

£450

5.

£7

6.

£3·50

Write how many 1p coins are needed to buy each item.

7.

£8

8.

£32

9.

£15

10.

£110

11.

£270

12.

£12·50

PS

Name ....

Multiplying and dividing by 10 and 100

Write the missing numbers.

1. 47 × 10 = ...

2. 850 ÷ 10 = ...

3. 7300 ÷ 10 = ...

4. 64 × 10 = ...

5. 9 × 100 = ...

6. 800 ÷ 100 = ...

7. 27 × 100 = ...

8. 6300 ÷ 100 = ...

9. .... × 10 = 830

10. .... ÷ 10 = 79

11. .... × 10 = 5200

12. .... ÷ 10 = 432

13. .... × 100 = 1800

14. .... ÷ 100 = 13

15. 84 × .... = 8400

16. 830 × 100 = ...

17. .... × 100 = 4600

18. .... ÷ 100 = 7

19. 160 × 100 = ...

20. 60 000 ÷ 100 = ...

PS

Multiplying decimals

> Each insect has been zapped by a ray-gun to be 100 times larger. Write the new length and width.

1. Beetle
    Length: 3·4 cm
    Width: 1·3 cm

    ----

2. Fly
    Length: 4·2 cm
    Width: 2·1 cm

    ----

3. Bee
    Length: 4·6 cm
    Width: 1·9 cm

    ----

4. Wasp
    Length: 5·3 cm
    Width: 1·9 cm

    ----

5. Worm
    Length: 8·6 cm
    Width: 1·1 cm

    ----

6. Ant
    Length: 0·4 cm
    Width: 0·2 cm

    ----

7. Stick Insect
    Length: 9·4 cm
    Width: 2·2 cm

    ----

8. Caterpillar
    Length: 6·7 cm
    Width: 3·1 cm

    ----

9. Grasshopper
    Length: 5·8 cm
    Width: 2·9 cm

> It takes each child 100 days to read all the pages in their book. If they read the same amount every day, how many pages did they read each day? How many pages is this, rounded to the nearest page?

10. 342 pages

    $342 \div 100 = 3\cdot42$ pages

    3 pages

11. 563 pages

    ----

12. 721 pages

    ----

13. 840 pages

    ----

14. 199 pages

    ----

15. 600 pages

    ----

16. 469 pages

    ----

17. 837 pages

    ----

18. 208 pages

Abacus Evolve Framework Edition Year 5 PCM © Harcourt Education Ltd 2007

PS

Common multiples

Use one colour to shade the multiples of 3.
Use a different colour to shade the multiples of 4.

1	2	3	4	5	6	7	8	9	10
11	12	13	14	15	16	17	18	19	20
21	22	23	24	25	26	27	28	29	30
31	32	33	34	35	36	37	38	39	40
41	42	43	44	45	46	47	48	49	50
51	52	53	54	55	56	57	58	59	60
61	62	63	64	65	66	67	68	69	70
71	72	73	74	75	76	77	78	79	80
81	82	83	84	85	86	87	88	89	90
91	92	93	94	95	96	97	98	99	100

Write the numbers that you have shaded in both colours:

Describe them: --

Try this for a different pair of multiples.

Abacus Evolve Framework Edition Year 5 PCM © Harcourt Education Ltd 2007

PS

Name _____

Circle graphs

The multiples of 2 are: 2, 4, 6, 8, 10, 12, 14, 16 …
Their units digits are: 2, 4, 6, 8, 0, 2, 4, 6 …
To draw a circle graph, join the units digits
in order, using a ruler.

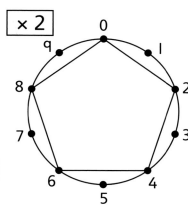

Draw circle graphs for the multiples of these numbers.

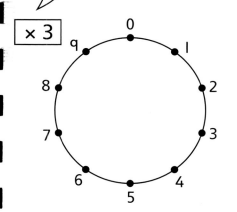

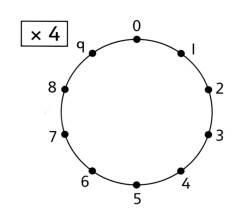

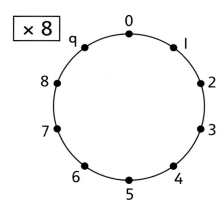

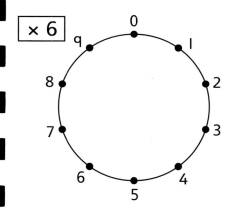

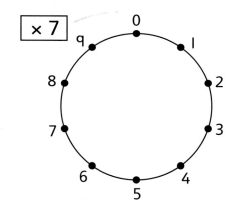

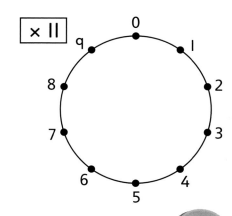

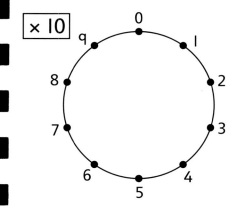

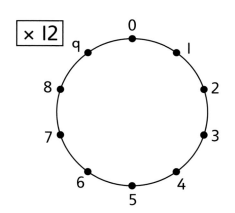

PS

Name _____

Multiplying

Shuffle a set of 2–9 number cards and place them face down in a pile. Turn over the first card, and write the number in the blank box in question I. Repeat for questions 2 to 8. Shuffle the cards again and repeat for questions 9 to 16.
Complete the multiplications.

I. ☐ × 20 = _____

2. ☐ × 50 = _____

3. ☐ × 30 = _____

4. ☐ × 90 = _____

5. ☐ × 400 = _____

6. ☐ × 300 = _____

7. ☐ × 70 = _____

8. ☐ × 700 = _____

9. ☐ × 200 = _____

10. ☐ × 60 = _____

II. ☐ × 600 = _____

12. ☐ × 500 = _____

13. ☐ × 40 = _____

14. ☐ × 800 = _____

15. ☐ × 80 = _____

16. ☐ × 900 = _____

Abacus Evolve Framework Edition Year 5 PCM © Harcourt Education Ltd 2007

PS

Name _____

Abacus Evolve Framework Edition Year 5 PCM © Harcourt Education Ltd 2007

Multiplying

> Roll a dice to find the multiplier for each question.
> If you roll a I, roll again. Complete the multiplications.

1. ☐ × 24 = (× 20) + (× 4)

    = ---------- + ---------- = ----------

2. ☐ × 32 = (× 30) + (× 2)

    = ---------- + ---------- = ----------

3. ☐ × 44 = (× 40) + (× 4)

    = ---------- + ---------- = ----------

4. ☐ × 37 = (× 30) + (× 7)

    = ---------- + ---------- = ----------

5. ☐ × 53 = (× 50) + (× 3)

    = ---------- + ---------- = ----------

6. ☐ × 28 = (× 20) + (× 8)

    = ---------- + ---------- = ----------

7. ☐ × 46 = (× 40) + (× 6)

    = ---------- + ---------- = ----------

PS

Name _____

Multiplying by 25

> Multiply by 25 by multiplying by 100, halving, and then halving again.

1. 48   4800   2400   48 × 25 = 1200

2. 16   _____   _____   16 × 25 = _____

3. 36   _____   _____   36 × 25 = _____

4. 24   _____   _____   24 × 25 = _____

5. 124   _____   _____   124 × 25 = _____

6. 28   _____   _____   28 × 25 = _____

> Multiply by 25 by halving, halving again, and then multiplying by 100.

7. 32   16   8   32 × 25 = 800

8. 64   _____   _____   64 × 25 = _____

9. 128   _____   _____   128 × 25 = _____

10. 404   _____   _____   404 × 25 = _____

11. 88   _____   _____   88 × 25 = _____

12. 148   _____   _____   148 × 25 = _____

Abacus Evolve Framework Edition Year 5 PCM © Harcourt Education Ltd 2007

PS

Name _____

Abacus Evolve Framework Edition Year 5 PCM © Harcourt Education Ltd 2007

Doubling and halving

$12 \times 22 = 264$

$15 \times 26 = 390$

$36 \times 24 = 864$

$28 \times 18 = 504$

$14 \times 48 = 672$

$40 \times 66 = 2640$

Use the multiplications above and doubling and halving to complete the following multiplications.

1. 6×22 = _____

2. $28 \times 36 =$ _____

3. 15×13 = _____

4. 28×9 = _____

5. 56×18 = _____

6. 14×96 = _____

7. 24×22 = _____

8. $20 \times 66 =$ _____

9. 56×9 = _____

10. 18×24 = _____

11. 7×48 = _____

12. $28 \times 24 =$ _____

13. $80 \times 66 =$ _____

14. 12×44 = _____

15. $30 \times 26 =$ _____

16. 18×12 = _____

PS

Name ....

Coordinate game

This is a game for two players, each with a set of counters of their own colour.
Take turns to roll two dice: the first represents the first (horizontal) coordinate, and the second represents the second (vertical) coordinate. Place a counter on the point, unless there is already a counter there. Continue taking turns. The winner is the first player to get four counters in any straight line.

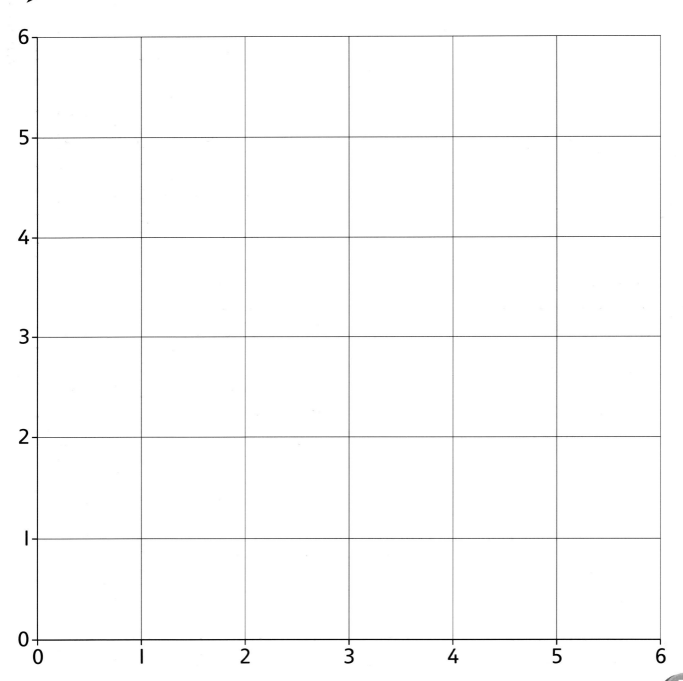

PS

Name

Abacus Evolve Framework Edition Year 5 PCM © Harcourt Education Ltd 2007

Translations

Draw the new position of the triangle after each of these translations. (You should draw six triangles.)

1. up 3

2. down 4

3. left 5

4. right 2

5. right 4, up 3

6. left 2, down 4

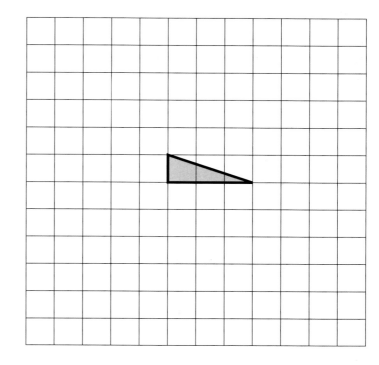

Draw and describe different translations of the rectangle.

7. --------------------------------

8. --------------------------------

9. --------------------------------

10. --------------------------------

11. --------------------------------

12. --------------------------------

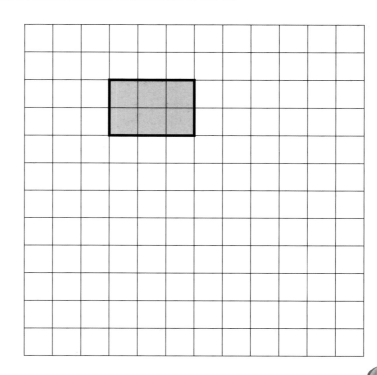

PS

Polygons

Draw three different polygons for each number of sides.
Write the name for a polygon with that number of sides.

1. 3 sides

   name: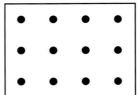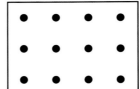

2. 4 sides

   name: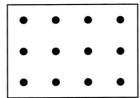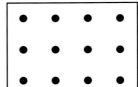

3. 5 sides

   name: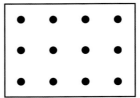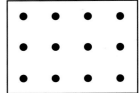

4. 6 sides

   name: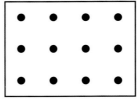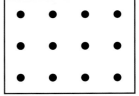

5. 7 sides

   name: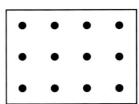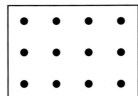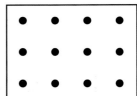

PS

Abacus Evolve Framework Edition Year 5 PCM © Harcourt Education Ltd 2007

Diagonals of a decagon

Draw all the diagonals of this regular decagon. Use a ruler!
Start by drawing all the diagonals from vertex A. Write how many you
have drawn in the box next to 'A'. Next draw as many new diagonals as
you can from vertex B. Write how many. Continue up to vertex J. Add
the 10 numbers together to find the total.

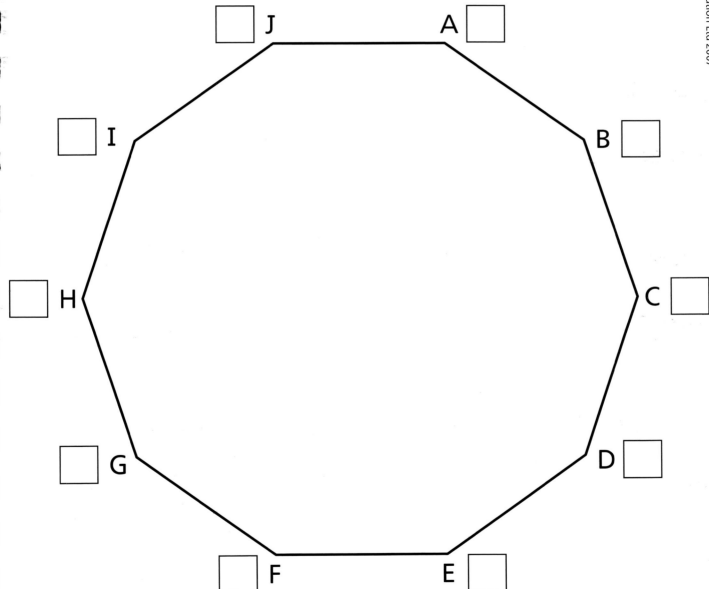

Total number of diagonals: _____

PS

Name _____

Area

Cut out 10 rectangles of the following sizes using card or paper.

6 cm × 8 cm	5 cm × 7 cm	6 cm × 6 cm	2 cm × 3 cm
4 cm × 9 cm	3 cm × 12 cm	7 cm × 8 cm	4 cm × 4 cm
8 cm × 5 cm	2 cm × 11 cm		

Cover as much of the grid as you can with them. Don't overlap any!
Write down how much of the floor is uncovered.
Repeat, but try to make the covered area as small as possible.

PS

Name _____

Abacus Evolve Framework Edition Year 5 PCM © Harcourt Education Ltd 2007

Tennis courts

These are the approximate measurements in metres of a tennis court.

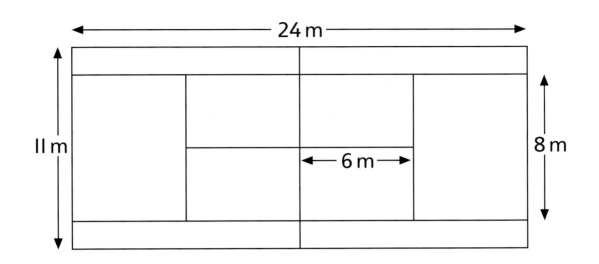

Calculate the areas of the shaded parts of the court.

1.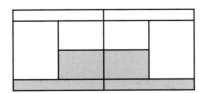

   Area: _____ m²

2.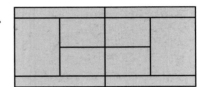

   Area: _____ m²

3.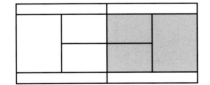

   Area: _____ m²

4.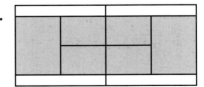

   Area: _____ m²

5.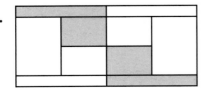

   Area: _____ m²

6.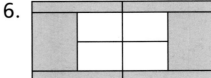

   Area: _____ m²

PS

Name

Perimeter of rectangles

Estimate the perimeter of each rectangle in millimetres. Measure each side with a ruler and calculate the perimeter. Write the difference in millimetres between your estimate and the actual perimeter.

1.

Estimate: _____ mm

Actual: _____ mm

Difference: _____ mm

2.

Estimate: _____ mm

Actual: _____ mm

Difference: _____ mm

3.

Estimate: _____ mm

Actual: _____ mm

Difference: _____ mm

4.

Estimate: _____ mm

Actual: _____ mm

Difference: _____ mm

5.

Estimate: _____ mm

Actual: _____ mm

Difference: _____ mm

6.

Estimate: _____ mm

Actual: _____ mm

Difference: _____ mm

PS

Name ....

Abacus Evolve Framework Edition Year 5 PCM © Harcourt Education Ltd 2007

Perimeter and area of squares

This table shows the area of some squares. Write the perimeters in cm.

Area of square	Perimeter of square
$4\,cm^2$	
$81\,cm^2$	
$25\,cm^2$	
$400\,cm^2$	
$36\,cm^2$	
$121\,cm^2$	

This table shows the perimeter of some squares. Write the areas in cm^2.

Perimeter of square	Area of square
$12\,cm$	
$80\,cm$	
$32\,cm$	
$120\,cm$	
$16\,cm$	
$48\,cm$	

PS

Units of time

> Write the equivalent number of seconds.

1. I min = ... secs

2. $1\frac{1}{2}$ mins = ... secs

3. 5 mins = ... secs

4. I hour = ... secs

5. I min, 26 secs = ... secs

> Write the equivalent number of minutes.

6. I hour = ... mins

7. $\frac{3}{4}$ hour = ... mins

8. $\frac{4}{5}$ hour = ... mins

9. $\frac{1}{2}$ day = ... mins

10. 2 hours, 57 mins = ... mins

> Write the equivalent number of hours.

11. I day = ... hours

12. $\frac{1}{3}$ day = ... hours

13. $2\frac{1}{2}$ days = ... hours

14. I week = ... hours

15. 4 days, 7 hours = ... hours

> Write the equivalent number of days.

16. 2 weeks = ... days

17. 60 hours = ... days

18. I year = ... days

19. November = ... days

20. March and April = ... days

PS

Name ....

Abacus Evolve Framework Edition Year 5 PCM © Harcourt Education Ltd 2007

Using a calendar

Look at the month below.

Monday	Tuesday	Wednesday	Thursday	Friday	Saturday	Sunday
1st	2nd	3rd	4th	5th	6th	7th
8th	9th	10th	11th	12th	13th	14th
15th	16th	17th	18th	19th	20th	21st
22nd	23rd	24th	25th	26th	27th	28th

Write the day of each of these birthdays

1. Sammy: 25th

----

2. Rover the dog: 13th

----

3. Granny: 16th

----

4. Chloe the cat: 5th

----

5. Mia: 10th

----

6. Ian: 28th

Solve these problems

7. The 1st of May is a Tuesday and Gala's birthday is on the 16th May. What day of the week is it on?

----

8. Sammy's granny is coming from India on Friday. Today is Monday 30th November. What date does she arrive?

----

9. Muna has to wait 25 days for a parcel. Today is Wednesday, 13th June. What day and date will her parcel get to her?

PS

Name ....

24-hour clock

Write each time as an am or pm time.

1.

   _2:28 pm_

2.

3.

4.

5.

6.

7.

8.

9.

10.

11.

12.

PS

Name ....

Abacus Evolve Framework Edition Year 5 PCM © Harcourt Education Ltd 2007

24-hour clock

Write these afternoon and evening times as 24-hour times.

1.

20:24

2.

3.

4.

5.

6.

7.

8.

9.

10.

11.

12.

PS

Name ....

Train timetable

Complete the timetable, assuming that the journey time for each stage is the same as for the first train.

Stations	1st train	2nd train	3rd train	4th train
Bobblewick	08:35	10:25	14:05	19:16
Plumtree	08:47			
Clutterbrook	08:56			
Orangeview	09:21			
Hilltop	09:37			
Bumblesea	09:58			
Dangleford	10:13			
Castlewall	10:32			
Littletoe	10:48			
Basham	11:07			

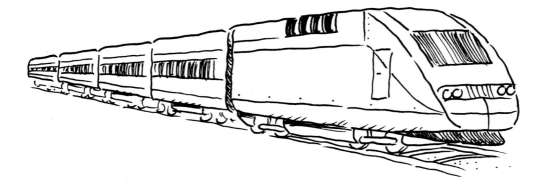

Name _____

Abacus Evolve Framework Edition Year 5 PCM © Harcourt Education Ltd 2007

Open the safe

Write the total of the numbers to open each safe.

1.

6   7
  3 ◎
8   4

Total: _____

2.

2   5
  7 ◎
9   8

Total: _____

3.

9   6
  7 ◎
9   3

Total: _____

4.

8   6
  5 ◎
4   7

Total: _____

5.

9   3
  7 ◎
6   8

Total: _____

6.

5   3
  2 ◎
7   9

Total: _____

7.

4   6
  8 ◎
5   9

Total: _____

8.

2   9
  8 ◎
8   8

Total: _____

9.

7   2
  5 ◎
9   6

Total: _____

10.

4   5
  7 ◎
9   3

Total: _____

11.

2   8
  9 ◎
1   7

Total: _____

12.

4   5
  6 ◎
9   9

Total: _____

PS

Name _____

Loads of money

Write the total of each set of money.

1.
£40 £50
£70 £30

Total: _____

2.
£80 £10
£90 £70

Total: _____

3.
£60 £70
£80

Total: _____

4.
£40 £80
£80 £60

Total: _____

5.
£90 £50
£70 £30

Total: _____

6.
£20 £90
£50 £80

Total: _____

7.
£70 £70
£80 £20 £70

Total: _____

8.
£30 £40
£90 £60 £70

Total: _____

9.
£80 £20
£10 £70 £90

Total: _____

10.
£60 £70
£80 £90 £30

Total: _____

11.
£80 £60
£60 £60 £40

Total: _____

12.
£70 £90
£90 £70 £70

Total: _____

PS

Name ....

Abacus Evolve Framework Edition Year 5 PCM © Harcourt Education Ltd 2007

Row and column totals

 Write the total of each row and column.

23	32	44	A
51	26	38	B
29	33	46	C

D E F

51	43	28	G
25	17	44	H
56	63	18	I

J K L

21	47	72	56	M
63	32	43	38	N
28	54	65	81	O
39	94	58	27	P

Q R S T

A   99 ....

B ....

C ....

D ....

E ....

F ....

G ....

H ....

I ....

J ....

K ....

L ....

M ....

N ....

O ....

P ....

Q ....

R ....

S ....

T ....

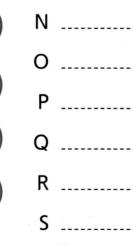

PS

Name ....

Adding near multiples of 10

Complete the tables.

	27	35	16	43	58	91	29	84
add 19								

	15	46	23	63	85	32	72	54
add 31								

	24	43	72	18	64	36	87	55
add 39								

	53	38	65	46	85	18	21	74
add 28								

	87	126	62	38	135	78	49	164
add 57								

Abacus Evolve Framework Edition Year 5 PCM © Harcourt Education Ltd 2007

PS

Name _____

Abacus Evolve Framework Edition Year 5 PCM © Harcourt Education Ltd 2007

Adding

Complete the additions.

1. 145 + 42   = _____

2. 173 + 26   = _____

3. 257 + 32   = _____

4. 237 + 44   = _____

5. 153 + 126   = _____

6. 174 + 113   = _____

7. 239 + 142   = _____

8. 244 + 138   = _____

9. 445 + 328   = _____

10. 436 + 237   = _____

11. 509 + 473   = _____

12. 684 + 207   = _____

13. 372 + 143   = _____

14. 564 + 372   = _____

15. 663 + 472   = _____

16. 194 + 285   = _____

17. 752 + 864   = _____

18. 534 + 963   = _____

19. 487 + 196   = _____

20. 369 + 275   = _____

PS

Name ....

Adding decimals

Complete the addition table.

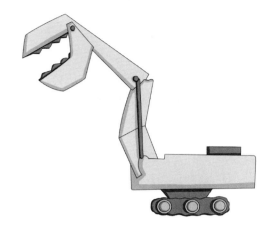

+	3·7	2·5	1·9	4·8
5·6	9·3			
7·2				
1·7				
2·9				
4·5				
1·32				
2·74				
5·08				

Abacus Evolve Framework Edition Year 5 PCM © Harcourt Education Ltd 2007

PS

Multiplying

Write an estimate for each multiplication in the loops.
Complete the multiplications.

1.

```
  1 2 6
×     4
_____
_____
```

2.

```
  2 1 7
×     3
_____
_____
```

3.

```
  3 4 2
×     5
_____
_____
```

4.

```
  4 3 4
×     6
_____
_____
```

5.

```
  5 7 3
×     3
_____
_____
```

6.

```
  2 8 9
×     4
_____
_____
```

7.

```
  7 1 7
×     5
_____
_____
```

8.

```
  3 8 6
×     7
_____
_____
```

9.

```
  2 9 4
×     3
_____
_____
```

Abacus Evolve Framework Edition Year 5 PCM © Harcourt Education Ltd 2007

Name ....

Multiplying

Shuffle a set of 2–9 number cards and select a card for each missing number below (you will need to use one card twice). Write the numbers in the boxes. Estimate the answers, and then complete the multiplications.

1.
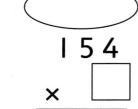

1 5 4

× ☐

_____

_____

2.
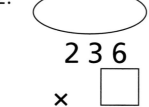

2 3 6

× ☐

_____

_____

3.
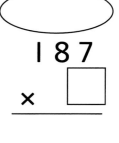

1 8 7

× ☐

_____

_____

4.
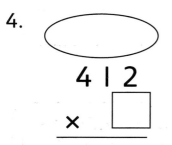

4 1 2

× ☐

_____

_____

5.
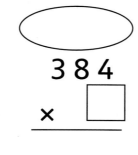

3 8 4

× ☐

_____

_____

6.
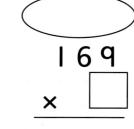

1 6 9

× ☐

_____

_____

7.
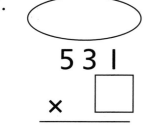

5 3 1

× ☐

_____

_____

8.
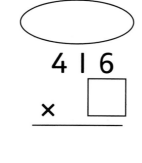

4 1 6

× ☐

_____

_____

9.

2 8 7

× ☐

_____

_____

PS

Name ....

Abacus Evolve Framework Edition Year 5 PCM © Harcourt Education Ltd 2007

Multiplying

Shuffle a set of 1–9 number cards and place them face down in a pile. Turn over the top card. Write the number in the first box in the first multiplication. Repeat until all nine boxes are filled.
Estimate the answers, and then complete the multiplications.

1.

$\times$ 4

_____

_____

_____

2.

$\times$ 7

_____

_____

_____

3.

$\times$ 6

_____

_____

_____

This time, decide which 1–9 number cards to place in each multiplication to create three multiplications that have an answer close to 2000. You must still only use the digits 1 to 9 once each!

4.

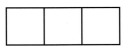

$\times$ 4

_____

_____

5.

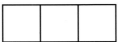

$\times$ 3

_____

_____

6.

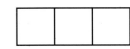

$\times$ 5

_____

_____

PS

Name ....

Multiplying

Complete the multiplications.

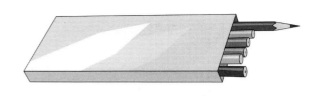

1. 17 × 10 = ...

2. 48 × 10 = ...

3. 10 × 41 = ...

4. 10 × 73 = ...

5. 14 × 20 = ...

6. 23 × 20 = ...

7. 28 × 30 = ...

8. 20 × 18 = ...

9. 30 × 17 = ...

10. 14 × 40 = ...

11. 42 × 30 = ...

12. 20 × 34 = ...

13. 30 × 56 = ...

14. 23 × 40 = ...

15. 50 × 18 = ...

16. 60 × 22 = ...

17. 14 × 70 = ...

18. 13 × 80 = ...

19. 40 × 16 = ...

20. 40 × 72 = ...

21. 27 × 50 = ...

22. 31 × 60 = ...

23. 42 × 80 = ...

24. 18 × 70 = ...

Abacus Evolve Framework Edition Year 5 PCM © Harcourt Education Ltd 2007

PS

Name ....

Abacus Evolve Framework Edition Year 5 PCM © Harcourt Education Ltd 2007

Multiplying

Write an estimate for each multiplication in the loops.
Complete the multiplications.

1.
$$\begin{array}{r} 27 \\ \times\ 18 \\ \hline \end{array}$$

2.
$$\begin{array}{r} 42 \\ \times\ 16 \\ \hline \end{array}$$

3.
$$\begin{array}{r} 35 \\ \times\ 17 \\ \hline \end{array}$$

4.
$$\begin{array}{r} 35 \\ \times\ 22 \\ \hline \end{array}$$

5.
$$\begin{array}{r} 46 \\ \times\ 27 \\ \hline \end{array}$$

6.
$$\begin{array}{r} 64 \\ \times\ 23 \\ \hline \end{array}$$

7.
$$\begin{array}{r} 54 \\ \times\ 33 \\ \hline \end{array}$$

8.
$$\begin{array}{r} 47 \\ \times\ 34 \\ \hline \end{array}$$

9.
$$\begin{array}{r} 56 \\ \times\ 38 \\ \hline \end{array}$$

PS

Name ....

Quarters and eighths

> Find one-quarter by halving, and then halving again.

1. $\frac{1}{2}$ of £48 = __£24__ $\Longrightarrow$ $\frac{1}{4}$ of £48 = __£12__

2. $\frac{1}{2}$ of £128 = _____ $\Longrightarrow$ $\frac{1}{4}$ of £128 = _____

3. $\frac{1}{2}$ of £192 = _____ $\Longrightarrow$ $\frac{1}{4}$ of £192 = _____

4. $\frac{1}{2}$ of £108 = _____ $\Longrightarrow$ $\frac{1}{4}$ of £108 = _____

5. $\frac{1}{2}$ of £252 = _____ $\Longrightarrow$ $\frac{1}{4}$ of £252 = _____

> Find one-eighth by halving, halving again and then halving again.

	$\frac{1}{2}$	$\frac{1}{4}$	$\frac{1}{8}$
6. £168 $\Longrightarrow$	£84 $\Longrightarrow$	£42 $\Longrightarrow$	£21
7. £264 $\Longrightarrow$	_____ $\Longrightarrow$	_____ $\Longrightarrow$	_____
8. £144 $\Longrightarrow$	_____ $\Longrightarrow$	_____ $\Longrightarrow$	_____
9. £368 $\Longrightarrow$	_____ $\Longrightarrow$	_____ $\Longrightarrow$	_____
10. £456 $\Longrightarrow$	_____ $\Longrightarrow$	_____ $\Longrightarrow$	_____

PS

Abacus Evolve Framework Edition Year 5 PCM © Harcourt Education Ltd 2007

Name ....

Abacus Evolve Framework Edition Year 5 PCM © Harcourt Education Ltd 2007

Fraction wheels

For each wheel, find each fraction of the amount in the centre, and write it in the outer ring.

A

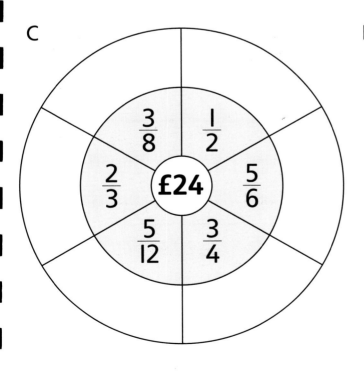

B

C

D

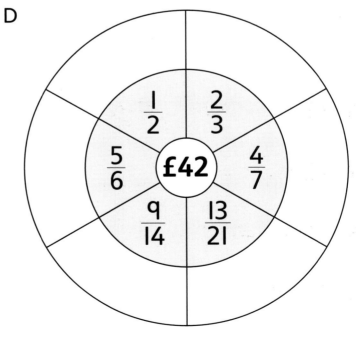

PS

Divisibility

Tick the boxes to show when the number is divisible without a remainder.

	÷10	÷100	÷2	÷5	÷4
48					
60					
90					
120					
240					
500					
87					
145					
168					
275					
840					
164					

PS

Name ....

Abacus Evolve Framework Edition Year 5 PCM © Harcourt Education Ltd 2007

Temperature

Write the new temperatures.

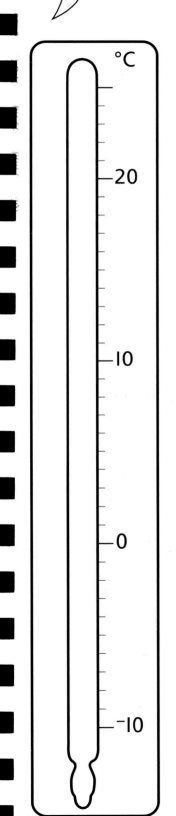

1. 14°C → down 7°C → up 2°C   ....

2. 6°C → up 2°C → down 11°C   ....

3. ⁻2°C → down 7°C → up 4°C   ....

4. 0°C → up 3°C → down 5°C   ....

5. 9°C → down 7°C → up 8°C   ....

6. ⁻8°C → up 4°C → down 2°C   ....

7. 4°C → down 9°C → up 3°C   ....

8. 1°C → up 7°C → down 10°C   ....

9. ⁻1°C → down 8°C → up 4°C   ....

10. ⁻5°C → up 9°C → down 6°C   ....

11. 5°C → up 18°C → down 13°C   ....

12. 23°C → down 21°C → up 7°C   ....

13. 11°C → down 9°C → down 7°C   ....

14. ⁻9°C → up 13°C → down 2°C   ....

15. 1°C → down 7°C → up 4°C   ....

PS

Positive and negative numbers

Write < or > between each pair of numbers.
Write the difference between the two numbers.

                     difference   **difference**

1. 7 $\boxed{>}$ 5   ...2...   2. 3 $\square$ 8   ....

3. ⁻6 $\square$ 4   ....   4. 5 $\square$ ⁻2   ....

5. ⁻3 $\square$ ⁻1   ....   6. ⁻2 $\square$ 7   ....

7. 3 $\square$ ⁻5   ....   8. ⁻1 $\square$ 1   ....

9. 2 $\square$ ⁻2   ....   10. 0 $\square$ ⁻3   ....

11. 6 $\square$ 0   ....   12. 9 $\square$ 11   ....

13. ⁻8 $\square$ ⁻18   ....   14. 7 $\square$ ⁻1   ....

15. 0 $\square$ 5   ....   16. ⁻2 $\square$ ⁻1   ....

17. 8 $\square$ 7   ....   18. ⁻6 $\square$ 0   ....

19. ⁻4 $\square$ ⁻3   ....   20. 1 $\square$ ⁻1   ....

Abacus Evolve Framework Edition Year 5 PCM © Harcourt Education Ltd 2007

Name ....

Rounding

Measure the length of each line in centimetres, using decimals. Round each length to the nearest centimetre.

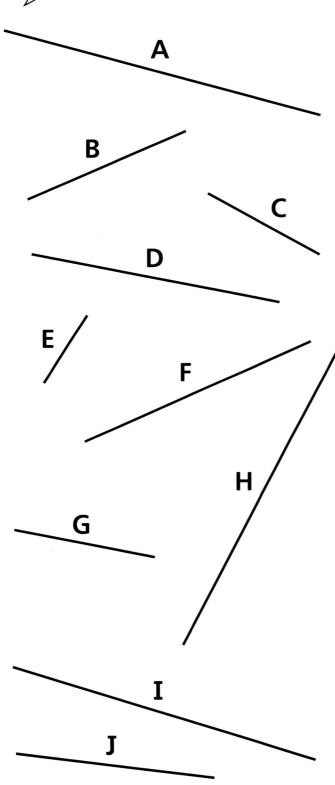

Line	Exact length	Rounded length
A	8·7 cm	9 cm
B		
C		
D		
E		
F		
G		
H		
I		
J		

Abacus Evolve Framework Edition Year 5 PCM © Harcourt Education Ltd 2007

PS

Name ....

Rounding

Choose three of the four digits each time to create decimal numbers that round to the whole numbers shown.

| 4 | 7 | 3 | q |

1. ☐ . ☐☐ ⟹ 7

2. ☐ . ☐☐ ⟹ 3

3. ☐ . ☐☐ ⟹ 8

4. ☐ . ☐☐ ⟹ 5

5. ☐ . ☐☐ ⟹ 4

6. ☐ . ☐☐ ⟹ q

7. ☐ . ☐☐ ⟹ 10

| 1 | 3 | 8 | 6 |

8. ☐ . ☐☐ ⟹ 6

9. ☐ . ☐☐ ⟹ 4

10. ☐ . ☐☐ ⟹ 1

11. ☐ . ☐☐ ⟹ q

12. ☐ . ☐☐ ⟹ 8

13. ☐ . ☐☐ ⟹ 2

14. ☐ . ☐☐ ⟹ 3

15. ☐ . ☐☐ ⟹ 7

PS

Name _____

Abacus Evolve Framework Edition Year 5 PCM © Harcourt Education Ltd 2007

Multiplying by 21 and 19

Write the cost of buying 21 of each item. Show your workings.

1.  18p

18 x 20 = 360
18 x 21 = 378
£3.78

2.  14p

_____

_____

_____

3. 32p

_____

_____

_____

4.  28p

_____

_____

_____

5.  56p

_____

_____

_____

6.  43p

_____

_____

_____

Write the cost of buying 19 of each item. Show your workings.

7.  17p

_____

_____

_____

8.  24p

_____

_____

_____

9.  36p

_____

_____

_____

10. 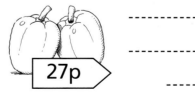 27p

_____

_____

_____

11.  44p

_____

_____

_____

12.  58p

_____

_____

_____

PS

The 17 times table

Complete these ×17 facts by doubling.

1. $1 \times 17 = \underline{\quad 17 \quad}$ 2. $2 \times 17 = \underline{\qquad}$

3. $4 \times 17 = \underline{\qquad}$ 4. $8 \times 17 = \underline{\qquad}$

5. $16 \times 17 = \underline{\qquad}$ 6. $32 \times 17 = \underline{\qquad}$

Use the answers above to help you complete these multiplications. Show your workings.

7. $9 \times 17 = \underline{\quad 136 + 17 \quad} = \underline{\quad 153 \quad}$

8. $5 \times 17 = \underline{\qquad\qquad\qquad} = \underline{\qquad}$

9. $7 \times 17 = \underline{\qquad\qquad\qquad} = \underline{\qquad}$

10. $17 \times 17 = \underline{\qquad\qquad\qquad} = \underline{\qquad}$

11. $33 \times 17 = \underline{\qquad\qquad\qquad} = \underline{\qquad}$

12. $12 \times 17 = \underline{\qquad\qquad\qquad} = \underline{\qquad}$

13. $24 \times 17 = \underline{\qquad\qquad\qquad} = \underline{\qquad}$

14. $18 \times 17 = \underline{\qquad\qquad\qquad} = \underline{\qquad}$

15. $28 \times 17 = \underline{\qquad\qquad\qquad} = \underline{\qquad}$

16. $25 \times 17 = \underline{\qquad\qquad\qquad} = \underline{\qquad}$

Abacus Evolve Framework Edition Year 5 PCM © Harcourt Education Ltd 2007

PS

Name ....

Abacus Evolve Framework Edition Year 5 PCM © Harcourt Education Ltd 2007

Multiplying

Find the area of each rectangle by splitting it into two smaller rectangles. Find the area of each of these rectangles, and then add the two together to find the total area.

1. 8 cm × 2·7 cm

$$
\begin{array}{cc}
 & 2 \quad \cdot7 \\
8 & \boxed{16 \;|\; 5\cdot6}
\end{array}
\qquad
\begin{array}{r}
16 \\
+ \quad 5\cdot6 \\
\hline
A = 21\cdot6 \text{ cm}^2
\end{array}
$$

2. 9 cm × 1·3 cm

3. 7 cm × 3·2 cm

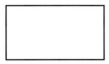

4. 6 cm × 2·4 cm

5. 11 cm × 2·3 cm

6. 9 cm × 4·3 cm

7. 8 cm × 3·8 cm

8. 6 cm × 3·9 cm

PS

Multiplying

Write an estimate for each multiplication in the loops.
Complete the multiplications.

1. 7 × 5·3

7 × 5   = _____

7 × 0·3 = _____

7 × 5·3 = _____

2. 9 × 3·7

9 × 3   = _____

9 × 0·7 = _____

9 × 3·7 = _____

3. 6 × 4·8

6 × 4   = _____

6 × 0·8 = _____

6 × 4·8 = _____

4. 3 × 8·4

3 × 8   = _____

3 × 0·4 = _____

3 × 8·4 = _____

5. 4 × 7·6

4 × 7   = _____

4 × 0·6 = _____

4 × 7·6 = _____

6. 9 × 4·9

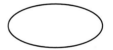

9 × 4   = _____

9 × 0·9 = _____

9 × 4·9 = _____

7. 8 × 3·8

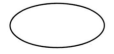

= _____

= _____

= _____

8. 9 × 6·4

= _____

= _____

= _____

9. 7 × 9·3

= _____

= _____

= _____

PS

Name _____

Abacus Evolve Framework Edition Year 5 PCM © Harcourt Education Ltd 2007

Adding 4-digit numbers

Write an estimate for each addition in the loops, and then complete the additions.

1.
```
  1 3 4 2
+ 2 5 1 6
---------
```

2.
```
  1 4 5 3
+ 4 3 2 8
---------
```

3.
```
  1 3 6 4
+ 7 4 5 2
---------
```

4.
```
  3 5 2 1
+ 2 9 6 3
---------
```

5.
```
  1 6 4 3
+ 3 2 7 5
---------
```

6.
```
  3 8 6 7
+ 3 7 2 1
---------
```

7.
```
  2 7 4 5
+ 1 8 3 6
---------
```

8.
```
  2 3 4 3
+ 5 4 7 9
---------
```

9.
```
  2 3 6 7
+ 1 9 8 1
---------
```

10.
```
  1 6 7 9
  2 3 5 8
+ 1 4 5 2
---------
```

11.
```
  1 2 3 6
  4 7 3 5
+ 1 5 2 8
---------
```

12.
```
  5 3 2 2
  4 1 3 6
+ 2 7 8 4
---------
```

PS

Name _____

Adding 4-digit numbers

A game for two or more players, each with a copy of this score sheet.
For each round, roll a dice eight times. After each throw, all players write the number in any one of their boxes. After the eighth throw, the players add their two 4-digit numbers together, and check each other's totals.
The player closest to 8000 scores 5 points, the next closest 4 points and so on. The winner is the player with most points after four rounds.

Round 1

score: ☐

Round 2

score: ☐

Round 3

score: ☐

Round 4

score: ☐

total score: _____

Name

Adding decimal numbers

Write an estimate for each addition in the loops, and then complete the additions.

1.

```
   1 · 3 6
 + 2 · 1 3
 _____
```

2.

```
   2 · 1 4
 + 1 · 3 7
 _____
```

3.

```
   5 · 4 8
 + 6 · 2 9
 _____
```

4.

```
   2 · 7 3
 + 6 · 4 5
 _____
```

5.

```
   1 4 · 5 9
 + 2 7 · 2 6
 _____
```

6.

```
    9 · 8 3
 + 1 1 · 7 4
 _____
```

7.

```
   8 · 5 6
 + 9 · 4 7
 _____
```

8.

```
   7 · 3 4
 + 6 · 8 9
 _____
```

9.

```
   4 · 6 5
 + 2 · 7 5
 _____
```

10.

```
   4 · 7 3
   2 · 1 4
 + 7 · 6 6
 _____
```

11.

```
   1 1 · 7 5
      9 · 4 1
 + 1 2 · 3 2
 _____
```

12.

```
   5 · 0 9
   7 · 3 2
 + 6 · 8 4
 _____
```

PS

Adding decimals game

A game for two or more players, each with a copy of this score sheet.
For each round, roll a dice six times. After each throw, all players write the
number in any one of their boxes. After the sixth throw, the players add their
two decimal numbers together, and check each other's totals.
The player with the largest total scores 5 points, the next largest 4 points,
and so on. The winner is the player with most points after four rounds.

Round 1

score:

Round 2

score:

Round 3

score:

Round 4

score:

total score: ....

Abacus Evolve Framework Edition Year 5 PCM © Harcourt Education Ltd 2007

PS

Name ....

Abacus Evolve Framework Edition Year 5 PCM © Harcourt Education Ltd 2007

Subtracting 3-digit numbers

Write an estimate for each subtraction in the loops, and then complete the subtractions.

1.
$$
\begin{array}{r}
4\ 7\ 6 \\
-\ 1\ 3\ 4 \\
\hline
\end{array}
$$

2.
$$
\begin{array}{r}
5\ 8\ 2 \\
-\ 3\ 6\ 1 \\
\hline
\end{array}
$$

3.
$$
\begin{array}{r}
7\ 5\ 4 \\
-\ 1\ 2\ 3 \\
\hline
\end{array}
$$

4.
$$
\begin{array}{r}
4\ 8\ 3 \\
-\ 2\ 1\ 5 \\
\hline
\end{array}
$$

5.
$$
\begin{array}{r}
7\ 6\ 4 \\
-\ 2\ 3\ 7 \\
\hline
\end{array}
$$

6.
$$
\begin{array}{r}
6\ 5\ 2 \\
-\ 3\ 1\ 8 \\
\hline
\end{array}
$$

7.
$$
\begin{array}{r}
3\ 2\ 7 \\
-\ 1\ 5\ 1 \\
\hline
\end{array}
$$

8.
$$
\begin{array}{r}
9\ 1\ 4 \\
-\ 3\ 6\ 2 \\
\hline
\end{array}
$$

9.
$$
\begin{array}{r}
4\ 3\ 4 \\
-\ 3\ 5\ 3 \\
\hline
\end{array}
$$

10.
$$
\begin{array}{r}
5\ 2\ 1 \\
-\ 2\ 3\ 8 \\
\hline
\end{array}
$$

11.
$$
\begin{array}{r}
9\ 3\ 4 \\
-\ 7\ 7\ 6 \\
\hline
\end{array}
$$

12.
$$
\begin{array}{r}
4\ 1\ 3 \\
-\ 2\ 5\ 9 \\
\hline
\end{array}
$$

PS

Name --

Subtracting

For each question, roll a dice three times to create a 3-digit number, and write it in the subtraction.
Estimate the answers, and then complete the subtractions.

1.
837
– _ _ _
_____

2.
925
– _ _ _
_____

3.
713
– _ _ _
_____

4.
1263
– _ _ _
_____

5.
1172
– _ _ _
_____

6.
2314
– _ _ _
_____

7.
4035
– _ _ _
_____

8.
2406
– _ _ _
_____

9.
3012
– _ _ _
_____

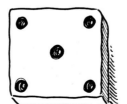

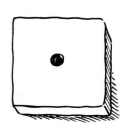

Abacus Evolve Framework Edition Year 5 PCM © Harcourt Education Ltd 2007

PS

Name ....

Abacus Evolve Framework Edition Year 5 PCM © Harcourt Education Ltd 2007

Subtracting

Write an estimate for each subtraction in the loops, and then complete the subtractions.

1.
```
  8 9 6 7
- 5 3 4 2
_____
```

2.
```
  7 5 8 6
-   3 6 1
_____
```

3.
```
  5 7 9 2
-   3 4 5
_____
```

4.
```
  3 9 7 1
- 1 2 3 8
_____
```

5.
```
  3 8 7 3
- 1 5 2 6
_____
```

6.
```
  5 6 1 8
- 2 2 4 3
_____
```

7.
```
  9 8 2 3
- 6 1 7 5
_____
```

8.
```
  7 3 1 2
- 2 1 5 7
_____
```

9.
```
  7 2 1 8
- 3 5 6 3
_____
```

10.
```
  3 4 5 6
- 1 7 8 2
_____
```

11.
```
  6 2 0 5
- 5 4 7 1
_____
```

12.
```
  5 3 2 1
- 1 8 4 7
_____
```

PS

Name _____

Subtracting decimal numbers

Write an estimate for each subtraction in the loops, and then complete the subtractions.

1.
```
   8 · 7 6
 − 3 · 5 2
 _____

 _____
```

2.
```
   9 · 4 2
 − 5 · 3 1
 _____

 _____
```

3.
```
   7 · 9 1
 − 2 · 3 4
 _____

 _____
```

4.
```
   6 · 8 3
 − 1 · 5 7
 _____

 _____
```

5.
```
   6 · 9 1
 − 1 · 3 4
 _____

 _____
```

6.
```
   4 · 2 8
 − 2 · 5 1
 _____

 _____
```

7.
```
   6 · 3 7
 − 4 · 8 1
 _____

 _____
```

8.
```
   8 · 2 1
 − 3 · 9 1
 _____

 _____
```

9.
```
   6 · 1 4
 − 1 · 3 5
 _____

 _____
```

10.
```
   5 · 2 3
 − 2 · 9 8
 _____

 _____
```

11.
```
   4 · 1 3
 − 2 · 2 7
 _____

 _____
```

12.
```
   3 · 0 2
 − 1 · 8 5
 _____

 _____
```

PS

Name _____

Subtracting decimals game

A game for two or more players, each with a copy of this score sheet. For each round, roll a dice six times. After each throw, all players write the number in any one of their boxes. After the sixth throw, the players subtract the bottom number from the top number. If the top number is smaller than the bottom number, score 0 points. Otherwise, the answer to your subtraction is your score. The winner is the player with most points after four rounds.

Round 1

score: _____

Round 2

score: _____

Round 3

score: _____

Round 4

score: _____

total score: _____

Abacus Evolve Framework Edition Year 5 PCM © Harcourt Education Ltd 2007

PS

Name ....

Chances

Tick one box for each statement to describe the chance of it happening.

	Impossible	Unlikely	Likely	Certain
I will laugh today.				
I will eat chips tonight.				
One day I will go to America.				
Tomorrow it will snow.				
The next person I see will be a boy.				
Next year I will be older.				
Next week I will be younger.				
One day I will be rich.				
One day I will be married.				
I will fall over tomorrow.				

Abacus Evolve Framework Edition Year 5 PCM © Harcourt Education Ltd 2007

PS

Name ....

Abacus Evolve Framework Edition Year 5 PCM © Harcourt Education Ltd 2007

Chance line

Decide how likely each event is, and then draw arrows and write the letters to position each event on the chance line.

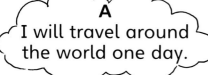

H

Impossible   Certain

A
I will travel around the world one day.

B
I will watch TV tonight.

D
It will be dark tonight.

C
I will be famous one day.

E
Tomorrow it will rain.

F
I will eat beans tonight.

G
I will have a drink tomorrow.

H
I will see a dragon tomorrow.

I
Dogs will fly.

K
I will catch a cold next week.

J
We will move house next year.

PS

Name _____

Line graph

This table shows the height of a hot air balloon between 9 am and 4 pm.

Time	09:00	10:00	11:00	12:00	13:00	14:00	15:00	16:00
Height	0 m	30 m	40 m	80 m	90 m	70 m	70 m	50 m

Complete the line graph to show this information.

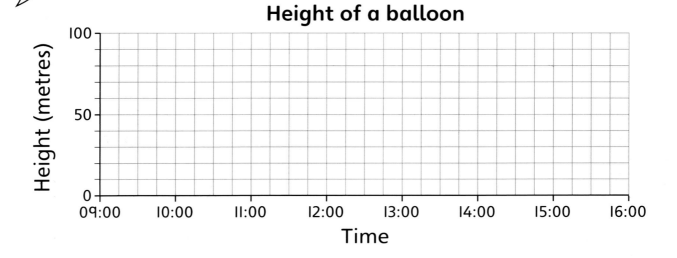

Height of a balloon

At what time is the balloon at:

1. its highest? _____

2. 70 m? _____

Write two times when the balloon is:

3. rising? _____

4. falling? _____

What is the balloon doing between:

5. 09:00 and 10:00? _____

6. 15:00 and 16:00? _____

Abacus Evolve Framework Edition Year 5 PCM © Harcourt Education Ltd 2007

PS

Name ....

Abacus Evolve Framework Edition Year 5 PCM © Harcourt Education Ltd 2007

Capacity scales

Colour up to the correct mark on each container to show the amount.

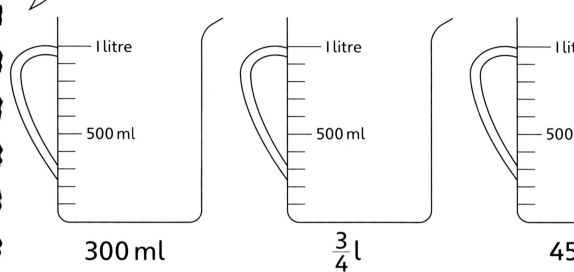

300 ml

$\frac{3}{4}$ l

450 ml

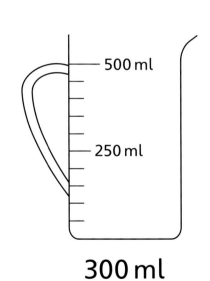

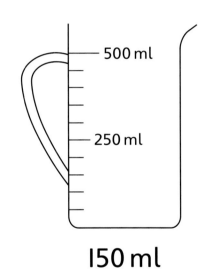

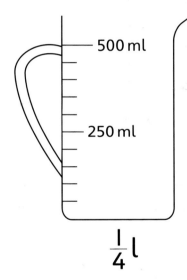

300 ml

150 ml

$\frac{1}{4}$ l

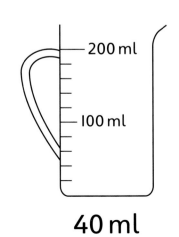

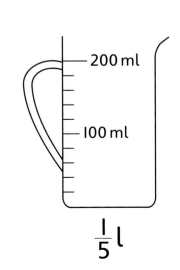

40 ml

$\frac{1}{5}$ l

125 ml

Litres, pints and gallons

- I pint is approximately $\frac{1}{2}$ litre.
- I gallon is approximately $4\frac{1}{2}$ litres.
- I gallon = 8 pints

Write <, > or = between each pair of amounts.

1. I pint ☐ 2 litres

2. 2 pints ☐ I litre

3. 5 pints ☐ 2 litres

4. 10 pints ☐ 4 litres

5. 3 litres ☐ 2 pints

6. 10 litres ☐ 5 pints

7. 2 gallons ☐ 10 litres

8. 10 gallons ☐ 50 litres

9. $\frac{1}{2}$ gallon ☐ 3 litres

10. 9 litres ☐ 2 gallons

11. 45 litres ☐ 10 gallons

12. 5 gallons ☐ 20 litres

13. 10 gallons ☐ 100 pints

14. 8 pints ☐ I gallon

15. $\frac{1}{2}$ gallon ☐ 2 litres

16. 4 pints ☐ $\frac{1}{2}$ gallon

PS

Name ....

Abacus Evolve Framework Edition Year 5 PCM © Harcourt Education Ltd 2007

Estimating and measuring angles

Estimate the size of each angle in degrees. Measure each angle using a protractor. Write the difference between each estimate and the actual angle. Which were your best estimates?

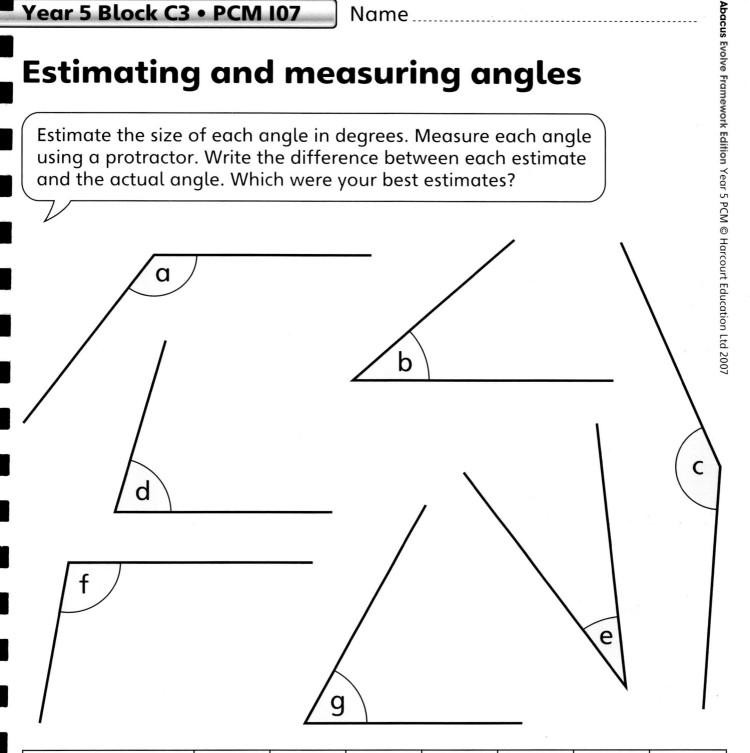

	a	b	c	d	e	f	g
Estimated							
Measured							
Difference							

PS

Name ....

Angles in a straight line

Write the missing angles.

1.
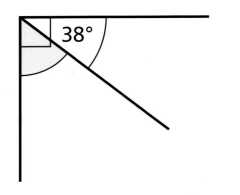
38°

2.
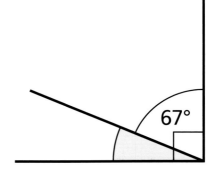
67°

3.
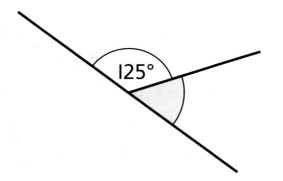
125°

4.
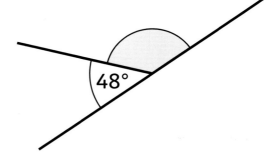
48°

5.
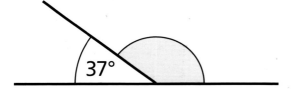
37°

6.
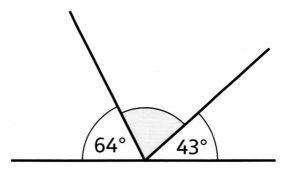
64°   43°

7.
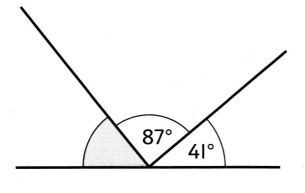
87°
41°

8.
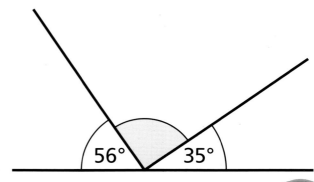
56°   35°

abacus Evolve Framework Edition Year 5 PCM © Harcourt Education Ltd 2007

Acute, obtuse and reflex angles

Colour the acute angles red, the obtuse angles blue and the reflex angles yellow.

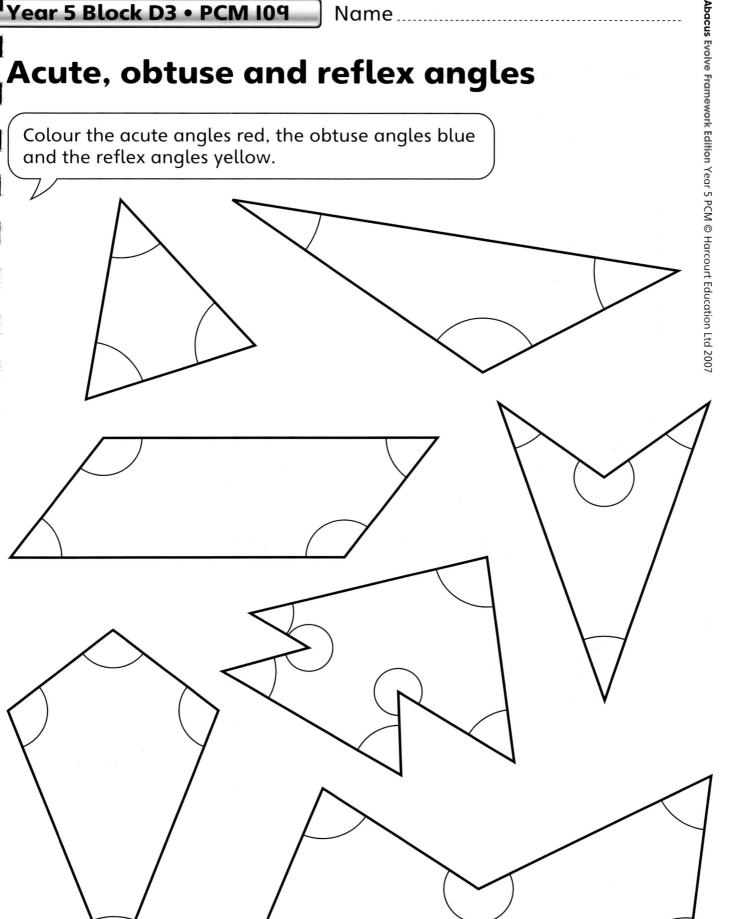

Abacus Evolve Framework Edition Year 5 PCM © Harcourt Education Ltd 2007

PS

Name ....

Angles of polygons

Join dots to draw the polygons described. Use a ruler!

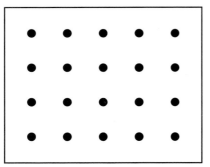

Triangle: 1 obtuse angle,
2 acute angles

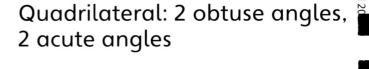

Quadrilateral: 2 obtuse angles,
2 acute angles

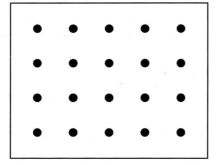

Quadrilateral: 1 reflex angle,
3 acute angles

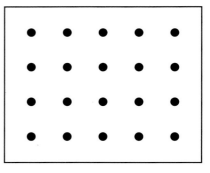

Pentagon: 2 right angles,
2 obtuse angles, 1 acute angle

Draw and describe your own polygons.

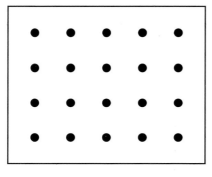

------------------- Block D3 • PCM 110 -------------------

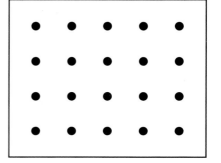

PS

Name ....

Abacus Evolve Framework Edition Year 5 PCM © Harcourt Education Ltd 2007

Dividing

Complete the divisions. Write estimates in the loops first.

1.
$87 \div 6 =$ ___ 14 r3

⟨15⟩

```
   87
 − 60    10 × 6
 ────
   27
 − 24     4 × 6
 ────
    3
```

2.
$47 \div 3 =$ ___

3.
$69 \div 4 =$ ___

4.
$91 \div 5 =$ ___

5.
$93 \div 8 =$ ___

6.
$87 \div 7 =$ ___

7.
$99 \div 8 =$ ___

8.
$83 \div 6 =$ ___

9.
$58 \div 4 =$ ___

Name ....

Dividing

Choose one 2-digit number between 80 and 100. Write your number in each division below. Complete the divisions, estimating first. How many divisions have a remainder? How many don't?

_____ ÷ 2 = _____	_____ ÷ 3 = _____	_____ ÷ 4 = _____
_____ ÷ 5 = _____	_____ ÷ 6 = _____	_____ ÷ 7 = _____
_____ ÷ 8 = _____	_____ ÷ 9 = _____	_____ ÷ 10 = _____

PS

Name _____

Abacus Evolve Framework Edition Year 5 PCM © Harcourt Education Ltd 2007

Dividing

Roll a dice for each question to find the divisor. If you roll a 1, roll again. Write the numbers in the boxes. Estimate the answers, and then complete the divisions.

147 ÷ ☐ = ----------

(   )

147

253 ÷ ☐ = ----------

(   )

253

161 ÷ ☐ = ----------

(   )

161

189 ÷ ☐ = ----------

(   )

189

217 ÷ ☐ = ----------

(   )

217

324 ÷ ☐ = ----------

(   )

324

PS

Name ....

Fractions to decimals

Write the equivalent decimal numbers.

1. $3\frac{7}{10}$ = ...

2. $4\frac{1}{10}$ = ...

3. $1\frac{37}{100}$ = ...

4. $5\frac{91}{100}$ = ...

5. $7\frac{3}{100}$ = ...

6. $2\frac{7}{100}$ = ...

7. $4\frac{1}{4}$ = ...

8. $6\frac{3}{4}$ = ...

9. $11\frac{6}{10}$ = ...

10. $11\frac{6}{100}$ = ...

11. $18\frac{1}{2}$ = ...

12. $1\frac{1}{4}$ = ...

13. $4\frac{53}{100}$ = ...

14. $\frac{117}{100}$ = ...

15. $\frac{29}{10}$ = ...

16. $\frac{46}{100}$ = ...

17. $\frac{8}{10}$ = ...

18. $5\frac{1}{5}$ = ...

19. $7\frac{3}{5}$ = ...

20. $8\frac{7}{20}$ = ...

PS

Name _____

Abacus Evolve Framework Edition Year 5 PCM © Harcourt Education Ltd 2007

Decimals and mixed numbers

Write each position as a decimal and a mixed number.

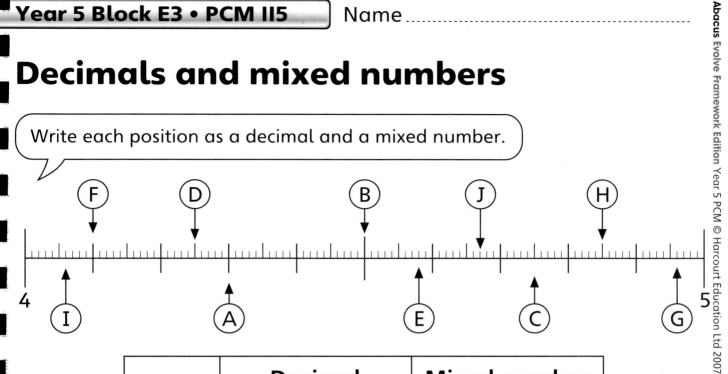

	Decimal	Mixed number
A	4·3	$4\frac{3}{10}$
B		
C		
D		
E		
F		
G		
H		
I		
J		

Name ....

Half-way numbers

Write the number exactly half-way between each pair.

1. 1·3, 1·5 ....

2. 2·4, 2·8 ....

3. 4·32, 4·36 ....

4. 7·22, 7·28 ....

5. 6·1, 6·2 ....

6. 7·9, 8·1 ....

7. 3·4, 3·7 ....

8. 8·9, 9·2 ....

9. 2·4, 3·1 ....

10. 2·62, $2\frac{74}{100}$ ....

11. $1\frac{3}{5}$, 1·72 ....

12. 4·6, 4·94 ....

13. $3\frac{3}{4}$, 3·95 ....

14. $5\frac{1}{4}$, 5·47 ....

15. 6·34, 7 ....

16. 9·62, 10·2 ....

17. 4·9, $5\frac{12}{100}$ ....

18. $7\frac{1}{10}$, $7\frac{28}{100}$ ....

PS

Name <u>   </u>

Abacus Evolve Framework Edition Year 5 PCM © Harcourt Education Ltd 2007

Percentages

Colour each grid to match the fraction. Write the percentage.

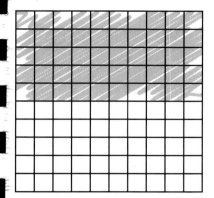

$\frac{1}{2}$ = <u>50%</u>

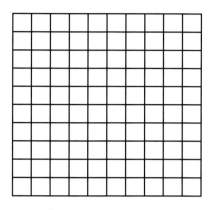

$\frac{1}{4}$ = <u>   </u>

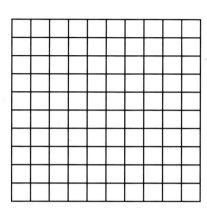

$\frac{3}{4}$ = <u>   </u>

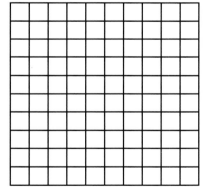

$\frac{7}{10}$ = <u>   </u>

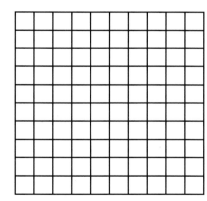

$\frac{1}{5}$ = <u>   </u>

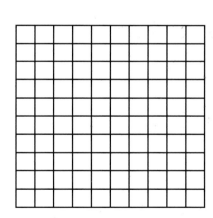

$\frac{4}{5}$ = <u>   </u>

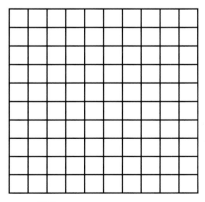

$\frac{17}{50}$ = <u>   </u>

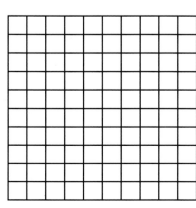

$\frac{13}{20}$ = <u>   </u>

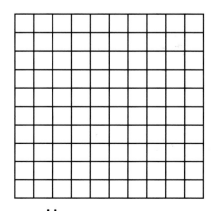

$\frac{11}{25}$ = <u>   </u>

PS

Name

Goals

These are the scores in 25 hockey matches, played by 50 teams. The home team's scores are always writtten first.

1 – 1	3 – 1	2 – 0	0 – 4	0 – 1
1 – 0	2 – 1	1 – 2	1 – 3	1 – 0
0 – 0	2 – 2	5 – 0	1 – 1	0 – 1
6 – 1	1 – 2	1 – 2	2 – 2	1 – 1
3 – 3	1 – 0	0 – 1	1 – 5	3 – 3

Write the percentage of teams that:

1. scored 2 goals   --------------

2. scored 1 goal   --------------

3. scored 3 goals   --------------

4. scored 0 goals   --------------

5. scored more than 2 goals   --------------

6. scored less than 2 goals   --------------

Write the percentage of matches:

7. that were draws   --------------

8. that were home wins   --------------

9. that were away wins   --------------

10. in which more than 4 goals were scored --------------

11. in which 3 or fewer goals were scored   --------------

PS

Name _____

Abacus Evolve Framework Edition Year 5 PCM © Harcourt Education Ltd 2007

Square numbers

Complete the number spiral.
Colour the squares that contain square numbers.

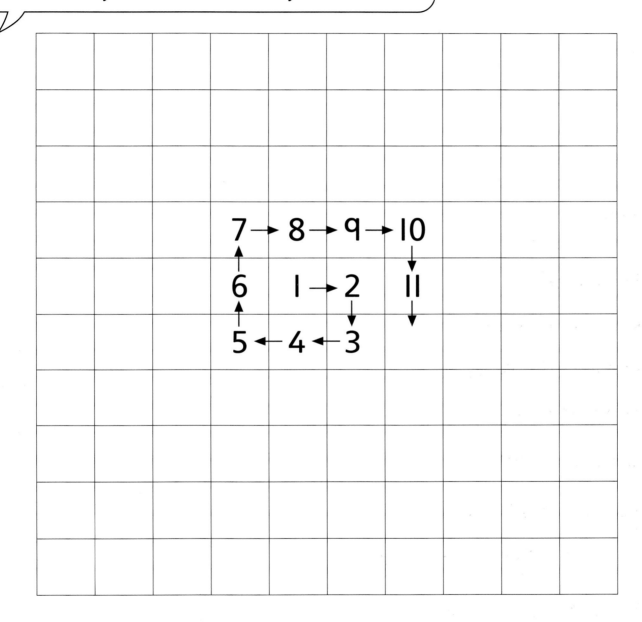

Describe any patterns.

Block E3 • PCM 119   Name _____

PS

Name ....

Square numbers

Write the numbers that give these answers when squared.

1. .... $^2 = 4$

2. .... $^2 = 100$

3. .... $^2 = 64$

4. .... $^2 = 25$

5. .... $^2 = 1$

6. .... $^2 = 49$

7. .... $^2 = 81$

8. .... $^2 = 9$

9. .... $^2 = 16$

10. .... $^2 = 36$

11. .... $^2 = 1600$

12. .... $^2 = 4900$

13. .... $^2 = 400$

14. .... $^2 = 8100$

15. .... $^2 = 2500$

16. .... $^2 = 10\,000$

17. .... $^2 = 6400$

18. .... $^2 = 900$

19. .... $^2 = 40\,000$

20. .... $^2 = 3600$

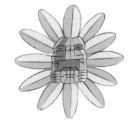

PS

Name _____

Odd one out

One number in each set is not a factor. Circle the odd one out.

Factors of **32**

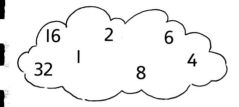

16   2   6
32   1
8   4

Factors of **36**

2   9   18   3
6   1
12   36   8   4

Factors of **40**

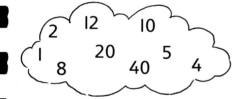

2   12   10
1   20   5
8   40   4

Factors of **18**

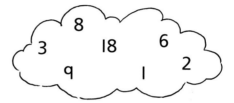

8
3   18   6
9   1   2

Factors of **26**

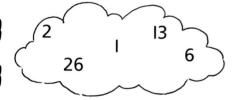

2   13
1
26   6

Factors of **45**

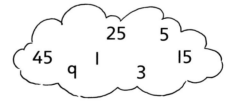

25   5
45   1   15
9   3

Invent two sets of your own, each with an odd one out.

Factors of _____

Factors of _____

Abacus Evolve Framework Edition Year 5 PCM © Harcourt Education Ltd 2007

PS

Name ....

Factors

Complete the lists of factors of each number from 30 to 50.

Number	Factors
30	1, 2, 3, 5, 6, 10, 15, 30
31	1, 31
32	
33	
34	
35	
36	
37	
38	
39	
40	
41	
42	
43	
44	
45	
46	
47	
48	
49	
50	

Abacus Evolve Framework Edition Year 5 PCM © Harcourt Education Ltd 2007

PS

Name

Changing multiplications

Complete the number sentences.

1. $8 \times 10 = 5 \times$ _____

2. $5 \times 6 = 10 \times$ _____

3. $14 \times 2 = 4 \times$ _____

4. $4 \times 9 = 2 \times$ _____

5. $8 \times 24 = 16 \times$ _____

6. $4 \times 6 = 3 \times$ _____

7. $2 \times 4 = 8 \times$ _____

8. $4 \times 12 = 6 \times$ _____

9. $2 \times 10 = 5 \times$ _____

10. $7 \times 34 = 14 \times$ _____

11. $6 \times 18 = 9 \times$ _____

12. $4 \times 16 = 8 \times$ _____

13. $12 \times 19 = 6 \times$ _____

14. $27 \times 14 = 7 \times$ _____

15. $18 \times 33 = 9 \times$ _____

16. $31 \times 24 = 12 \times$ _____

17. $32 \times 43 = 16 \times$ _____

18. $17 \times 40 = 10 \times$ _____

Abacus Evolve Framework Edition Year 5 PCM © Harcourt Education Ltd 2007

PS

Name ....

5-digit number game

for 2 children

A game for two players, with one set of number cards 0–9.
Deal five cards to each player. Place your cards in order to create a 5-digit number. Each player writes their number on their side of the sheet. Read each other's number aloud. If you read it correctly, you score points to match the total of the digits in that number (for example, if the other player's number is 35281, you would score 19).
The winner is the player with more points after four rounds.

Player A	score	**Player B**	score

Name ....

6-digit numbers

for 2 children

You need number cards 0–9.
Shuffle the cards and place them face down in a pile. Take one card each.
Work together to find out how many 6-digit numbers you can make using only these two numbers. You must use both numbers in every 6-digit number you make.
How do you know when you have found them all?
Would you be able to make the same number of 6-digit numbers if you had chosen two different number cards?

3 **7**   3377373, 333337, 333377, …

How many 5-digit numbers would you be able to make using just two numbers?

Paper strips

for 4 children

You need some long strips of paper.
The first person writes a 5-digit number at the top of a strip of paper. Fold it over so it is hidden. Pass it to the next person, who writes a 5-digit number below the folded part, then folds it over again to hide their number. Continue until everyone has written a number. Unfold the paper and read all the numbers together. Write the numbers in order, smallest to largest. Play again, but this time try to make it so the numbers appear written in order, smallest to largest, when the paper is unfolded. No cheating allowed!

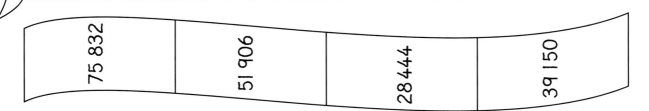

Abacus Evolve Framework Edition Year 5 PCM © Harcourt Education Ltd 2007

Populations and areas

for 2 children

Use the internet or an encyclopaedia to find the population of different countries. Write them in figures and words.

USA: 272 600 000

two hundred and seventy-two million, six hundred thousand

Find the area of some countries, and write them in figures and words.

Brazil: 8 511 965 km²

eight million, five hundred and eleven thousand, nine hundred and sixty-five square kilometres

Abacus Evolve Framework Edition Year 5 PCM © Harcourt Education Ltd 2007

Cube towers

for 3 children

You need number cards 1–10 and a large pile of cubes (up to 90). Shuffle the number cards and spread them out face down. One player reveals two numbers. You must all write these two numbers as a multiplication, and then work together to make cube towers to match – as quickly as you can! Add up your cubes, then write the multiplication. Is there a different way of arranging the cubes for the same multiplication? Reshuffle the cards and repeat.

5×3

$5 \times 3 = 15$

Multiplication game

for 4 children

This is a game for four players, in teams of two. You need a multiplication square, two sets of number cards 1–10 and a set of counters for each team in their own colour.
Shuffle the cards and place them in two piles, face down. Each team takes turns to reveal one card from each pile, and multiplies the numbers together. If possible, they place a counter on the matching number on the multiplication square. Continue taking turns. The winning team is the first to get three counters in a straight line.

1	2	3	4	5	6	7	8	9	10
2	4	6	8	10	12	14	16	18	20
3	6	9	12	15	18	21	24	27	30
4	8	12	16	20	●	28	32	36	40
5	10	15	20	25	30	35	40	45	50
6	12	18	24	○	36	42	48	54	60
7	14	21	28	35	42	49	56	63	70
8	16	24	32	40	48	56	64	72	80
9	●	27	36	45	54	63	○	81	90
10	20	30	40	50	60	70	80	90	100

Name _____

Remainder patterns

for 2 or 3 children

Divide each of the numbers in the multiplication square by 4. Write the remainder after each division in the matching square in the right-hand grid.

1	2	3	4	5	6	7	8	9	10
2	4	6	8	10	12	14	16	18	20
3	6	9	12	15	18	21	24	27	30
4	8	12	16	20	24	28	32	36	40
5	10	15	20	25	30	35	40	45	50
6	12	18	24	30	36	42	48	54	60
7	14	21	28	35	42	49	56	63	70
8	16	24	32	40	48	56	64	72	80
9	18	27	36	45	54	63	72	81	90
10	20	30	40	50	60	70	80	90	100

1	2	3	0	1	2	3	0	1	2
2	0	2							

Abacus Evolve Framework Edition Year 5 PCM © Harcourt Education Ltd 2007

Name _____

Remainders as fractions and decimals

for 2 children

You need two dice.
Take turns to throw the two dice to create your own 2-digit number. You must then each write a division involving your number, which will give a remainder which can be written as a fraction and as a decimal.

  $43 \div 5 = 8\frac{3}{5}$ or 8·6

Check each other's multiplications. Can any of these fractions be simplified?

Repeat until you have each written 10 multiplications.

Abacus Evolve Framework Edition Year 5 PCM © Harcourt Education Ltd 2007

Name _____

Odd and even Carroll diagram

for 2 children

You need two sets of number cards 0–9.
Draw a Carroll diagram like this, which you will share.

	odd	even
less than 500		
500 or more		

Shuffle the number cards and place them face down in a pile. Take three cards each. Use your numbers to create a 3-digit number. Both write your numbers in the correct part of the Carroll diagram. Check each other's. Repeat several times, reshuffling the cards each time. The first person to write a number in each of the four sections of the diagram wins!
Draw a new Carroll diagram and play again.

- -

Name _____

Odd and even totals

for 2 children

Investigate vertical pairs of numbers on this grid. How many have an odd total? How many have an even total?

21	30	19	12	25
15	27	11	31	18
17	20	24	13	29
34	32	14	22	35
23	16	28	33	26

21
15

Repeat for horizontal pairs of numbers.

21	30

Investigate the totals of horizontal and vertical triplets.

21	30	19

21
15
17

Abacus Evolve Framework Edition Year 5 PCM © Harcourt Education Ltd 2007

Counting game

for 4 or 5 children

You need hundreds and tens place-value cards. Shuffle and place them face down in two piles. Choose a multiple of 5 to be your jump size, for example 15. Reveal one of each type of card to create a 3-digit number, for example 320.

$$3 \mid 2 \ 0 >$$

The first person says the next number in the sequence, starting at 320 and adding 15: *three hundred and thirty-five*. Go round the group, adding 15s, until everyone has had two turns.
Each person then writes the sequence.

320, 335, 350, 365, 380

Repeat for different start numbers and different jump sizes. Include jumping backwards.

Abacus Evolve Framework Edition Year 5 PCM © Harcourt Education Ltd 2007

Square numbers and digital roots

for 2 children

A square number is the result of a number multiplied by itself.

$$4^2 = 4 \times 4 = 16$$

Work together to find the first 16 square numbers (from 1×1 to 16×16). Find the digital root of each square number by adding the digits together until you get a single digit answer.

digital root of $16 = 1 + 6 = 7$

Continue the sequence of square numbers and continue finding the digital roots. Can you see a pattern?

Perpendicular line patterns   for 2 children

You need some large sheets of
squared paper.
One of you draws a line of any
length on the squared paper, using a
ruler. The other draws a line
perpendicular (at right angles) to it,
touching the first line at one point.
The first person then draws another
line, touching either of the first two
lines at one point, and perpendicular
to it. Continue like this until you
have created an interesting pattern.
If you like, you can use colours to
create an artistic effect.

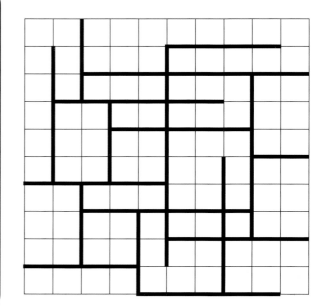

Shapes with parallel sides   for 2 children

Use 5 × 5 squares of dots on dotty paper.
Draw different polygons with one pair of parallel sides.
Draw different polygons with two pairs of parallel sides.
Draw different polygons with three pairs of parallel sides.
Have you found all the possible examples?
Try to name each polygon.

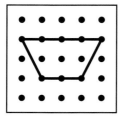 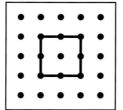 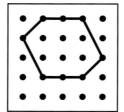

Draw as many different polygons as you can with:
one pair of perpendicular lines; two pairs of perpendicular lines;
three pairs of perpendicular lines.
Have you found them all?

Isosceles triangles

for 2 children

Use 4 × 3 rectangles of dots on dotty paper.
Draw five different isosceles triangles.

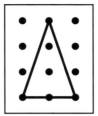

Draw five different scalene triangles.

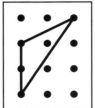

Draw five different right-angled triangles.

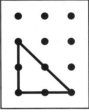

Abacus Evolve Framework Edition Year 5 PCM © Harcourt Education Ltd 2007

Matchstick triangles

for 2 children

You need I5 matchsticks.
Work together to arrange the I5 matchsticks to make a triangle. You must use all I5! Write the number of matchsticks on each side. What type of triangle is it? Make as many different triangles as you can. Write down the number of matchsticks on each side for each one. Make three lists of all the side lengths, sorted into equilateral, isosceles and scalene.

3, 6, 6
isosceles

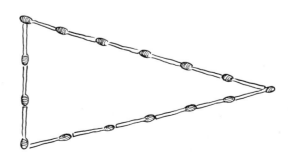

Abacus Evolve Framework Edition Year 5 PCM © Harcourt Education Ltd 2007

Your graph

for 2 children

Invent a title for this graph.
Label the axes.
Label the five bar lines.

Write six questions about your graph.

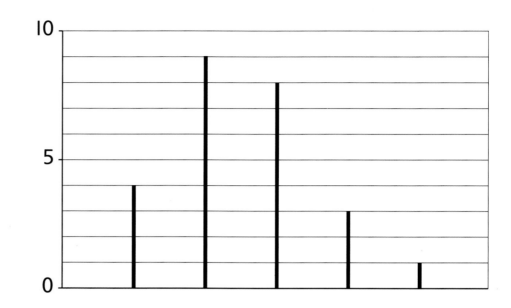

Music graph

for 2 children

You need a selection of music CDs.
Look at the length of each track on the CDs. Round each one to the nearest minute. Record about 20 rounded track lengths in a table.
Create a bar line graph to display the information. Start off like this:

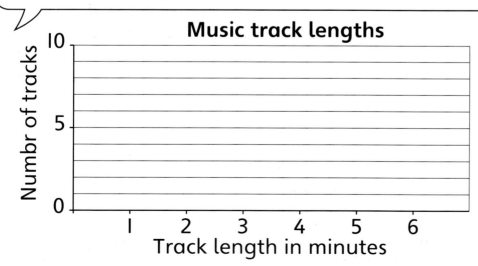

What is the mode track length?

Abacus Evolve Framework Edition Year 5 PCM © Harcourt Education Ltd 2007

Name ....

Map reading

for 3 or 4 children

You need a road map and a ruler.

Check the scale on the map, for example I cm might represent 2 km. Choose two places on the map, and measure the distance between them in centimetres, using the ruler. Use the scale to work out the real distance in kilometres.

Find the approximate distance in miles. Remember, 5 miles is about 8 km!

Record the distances in a chart.

	Distance in km	Distance in miles
Satbury to Chipwell	14·8 km	9 miles

Abacus Evolve Framework Edition Year 5 PCM © Harcourt Education Ltd 2007

Name ....

Furniture measurements

for 4 children

You need a furniture catalogue.

Choose a piece of furniture in the catalogue and write its name and measurements. Then convert the measurements into a different unit of length. For example, if the measurements are in centimetres, change them to metres.

Do this for I0 pieces of furniture.

Dining table

	Length	Width	Height
Centimetres	I50 cm	90 cm	75 cm
Metres	I·5 m	0·9 m	0·75 m

Abacus Evolve Framework Edition Year 5 PCM © Harcourt Education Ltd 2007

Ingredients

for 4 children

You need a recipe book for cakes, biscuits and breads.
Choose a recipe from the book. Write all the weights from the ingredients list in grams. Then work out how much of each ingredient you need to make the recipe for 10 times as many people! Write the new quantities in grams, and then convert them to kilograms.

Ingredient	4 people (g)	40 people (g)	40 people (kg)
Plain flour	250 g	2500 g	2·5 kg

Posting letters and parcels

for 3 or 4 children

This table shows postage prices for sending letters and parcels within Britain.
Find 10 flat items of different weights up to 750 g. Investigate how much it would cost to post each item by first-class post, and by second-class post.
Record your findings in a simple table.

Maximum weight	First class	Second class
60 g	30p	21p
100 g	46p	35p
150 g	64p	47p
200 g	79p	58p
250 g	94p	71p
300 g	£1·07	83p
350 g	£1·21	94p
400 g	£1·40	£1·14
450 g	£1·59	£1·30
500 g	£1·78	£1·48
600 g	£2·15	£1·75
700 g	£2·52	£2·00
750 g	£2·71	£2·12

Abacus Evolve Framework Edition Year 5 PCM © Harcourt Education Ltd 2007

Tile patterns

for 2 children

Make four identical square tiles like these out of card.

Place the four tiles together to make a 2 × 2 square with a symmetrical pattern.
Investigate different patterns.

Repeat for a different set of tiles with a symmetrical pattern, for example:

Abacus Evolve Framework Edition Year 5 PCM © Harcourt Education Ltd 2007

Circle patterns

for 2 children

You need six identical circles drawn on paper (use PCM I82).
You will need to join the points on each circle using straight lines.
First circle: join every second point. Draw a line from the top point to the second point (always count clockwise), then the second to the fourth, fourth to sixth, sixth to eighth. Stop when you get back to the starting point.
Second circle: join every third point.
Third circle: join every fourth point.
And so on until you have joined every seventh point.
Look at each pattern. How many lines of symmetry does each one have?

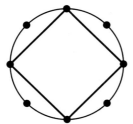 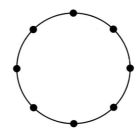

Abacus Evolve Framework Edition Year 5 PCM © Harcourt Education Ltd 2007

Making a tetrahedron

for 2 children

You need two sheets of isometric dotty paper.
Draw a large equilateral triangle each on your sheet of dotty paper.
Check each other's to make sure all the sides and angles are equal. On your own triangle, join the mid-points of each side, to create 4 equilateral triangles. Cut out the large triangle and fold along the lines. Decorate it, and then stick it together to make a tetrahedron.

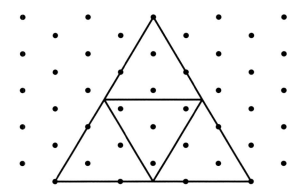

Labelling and sorting shapes for 2 or 3 children

You need a set of 3D shapes, and some labels made of card.
Place the shapes in a line. Make a label for each shape: write the name of the shape and the number of faces, vertices and edges.

PYRAMID
5 faces,
5 vertices,
8 edges

When the shapes have all been labelled, find different ways of sorting them, for example:
'even number of faces' v 'odd number of faces'
'eight or more edges' v 'fewer than eight edges'
'has a triangular face' v 'does not have a triangular face'.

Abacus Evolve Framework Edition Year 5 PCM © Harcourt Education Ltd 2007

Making 10

for 4 children

This game is for four people, playing in pairs.
You need units, tenths and hundredths place-value cards, and a pile of coins.
Shuffle the cards and place them face down in three piles. Each pair selects one card from each pile to create a 2-place decimal number.

Write what must be added to your number to make 10.

$$\boxed{7} \boxed{\cdot5} \boxed{3} \!>$$

$7 \cdot 53 + 2 \cdot 47 = 10$

If your answer is correct, collect a number of 1p coins to match the units digit of the number to be added. For example, if you added 2·47, you would collect 2p. Play 10 rounds. The winner is the pair who collect most money!

Abacus Evolve Framework Edition Year 5 PCM © Harcourt Education Ltd 2007

Adding decimal numbers to make 10   for 2 or 3 children

You need two sets of number cards 0–9.
Shuffle all the cards into one pack, and deal two cards to each player. Use your cards to make a decimal number with one decimal place. You can choose which card you use for the units, and which for the tenths. Write down your number. All check that everyone's written numbers match their cards! Put all the cards to the bottom of the pack and reshuffle. Deal two more cards to each player. Use your cards to make another 1-place decimal number. The aim is to total 10 when you add this number to your first number. Add your two numbers together. Anyone who gets a total of 10 scores 10 points!
Repeat several times. Who scores the most points?

$$\boxed{2} \cdot \boxed{6} + \boxed{7} \cdot \boxed{4} = 10$$

Difference pairs

for 4 children

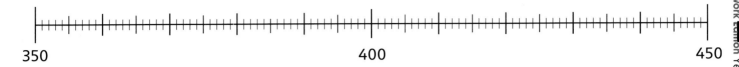

350   400   450

> This game is for four people, playing in pairs.
> You need number cards 0–30. Shuffle the cards and place them face down in a pile. Each pair takes turns to reveal a card. They then write a pair of numbers, either side of 400, that have that difference. Use the number line to help you.
> Play 10 rounds, trying not to repeat a number.

For example: | 14 | $405 - 391 = 14$

Adding to the next thousand

for 2 children

> You need number cards 10–99 and cubes.
> Shuffle the cards and place them face down in a pile. Take two cards each. Use your two numbers to create a 4-digit number. For example, if you selected 24 and 37, your number would be 2437 or 3724 – you can choose which. Work out how much more it is to the next thousand, and record the addition. Compare how much each of you added onto your 4-digit number. The player whose added amount is nearest 500 takes a cube.
> Play several rounds, reshuffling the cards between each round. Who won more cubes?

| 24 | 37 | $3724 + 276 = 4000$

Abacus Evolve Framework Edition Year 5 PCM © Harcourt Education Ltd 2007

Name _____

Abacus Evolve Framework Edition Year 5 PCM © Harcourt Education Ltd 2007

Halving

for 2 children

You need tens and units place-value cards (use only the even units cards). Shuffle the cards. Take one card from each set to create a 2-digit number. One of you should halve the tens. The other should halve the units. Add your answers together to find half of the whole number.
Do this ten times.

| 2 | 6 |

half of 20 = 10
half of 6 = 3

10 + 3 = 13
half of 26 = 13

Name _____

Abacus Evolve Framework Edition Year 5 PCM © Harcourt Education Ltd 2007

Dartboard scores

for 2 or 3 children

On this dartboard, you score double if your dart lands in the outer ring.
Investigate all the possible total scores when you throw two darts.
Which scores, less than 10, are not possible?

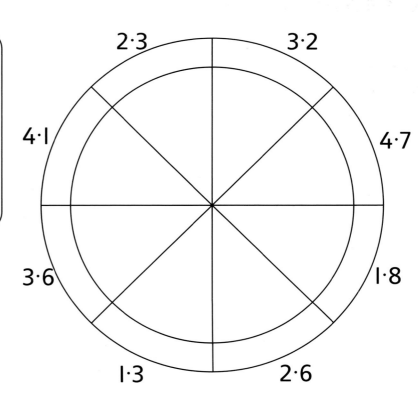

Double the difference

for 2 or 3 children

You need tens and hundreds place-value cards.
Select two of each type of card to make two 3-digit numbers. Find double the difference between the numbers in two ways:
(1) Find the difference between the two numbers, and then double it.
(2) Double each number, and then find the difference.
Try both methods for five different pairs of numbers. What do you notice?

| 5 | 3 | 0 | | 3 | 7 | 0 |

$530 - 370 = 160 \implies 160 \times 2 = 320$
$530 \times 2 = 1060 \implies 370 \times 2 = 740 \implies 1060 - 740 = 320$

Repeat, but find double the total, instead of double the difference.

Partitioning

for 2 children

You need number cards 0–9.
Shuffle the cards and spread them out face down. Select three cards. Use them to create a 3-digit even number. If you can't make an even number, swap one card for a different one. You must decide how to split the number between you – one person could be 'hundreds' and the other 'tens and units', or one could be 'hundreds and tens' and the other could be 'units'. Each look at your part of the number, and double it. Add your answers together to find the double of the whole number. Now try halving the number by halving a part each. You can check your answers using a calculator: multiply the halved number by 4 – it should equal the doubled number. If it doesn't, work out where you went wrong!
Repeat the activity several times.

double 500 = 1000
double 28 = 56
1000 + 56 = 1056

| 5 | 2 | 8 |

half of 500 = 250
half of 28 = 14
250 + 14 = 264

Abacus Evolve Framework Edition Year 5 PCM © Harcourt Education Ltd 2007

Ordering mixed numbers   for 4 or 5 children

You need a set of number cards 1–20 and a pile of counters or cubes. Deal two cards to each player. Each player creates an improper fraction by using their larger number as the numerator and the smaller number as the denominator. Then, each write your fraction as a mixed number. Check each other's answers. The player with the largest number wins five counters, the next largest wins four, and so on. Repeat for several rounds. The player with the most counters is the winner!

$$\frac{11}{3} = 3\frac{2}{3}$$

Abacus Evolve Framework Edition Year 5 PCM © Harcourt Education Ltd 2007

Improper fractions to mixed numbers   for 2 children

You need nine 10p coins. Each of you writes an improper fraction. The denominator must not be 2 or 4! Convert each other's fraction to a mixed number. Then compare the fraction that is left over.
Whoever has the fraction nearest to one-half takes a 10p coin. Keep playing until one player has collected 50p.

Player A	Player B
$\frac{45}{7}$	$\frac{21}{5}$
$\frac{45}{7} = 6\frac{3}{7}$	$\frac{21}{5} = 4\frac{1}{5}$
$\frac{3}{7}$ left over	$\frac{1}{5}$ left over

Name ....

Ordering fractions

for 3 or 4 children

Cut out these eight fractions. Put them in order, smallest to largest. Discuss why one is smaller than another.

$\frac{3}{4}$	$\frac{5}{8}$	$\frac{3}{16}$	$\frac{1}{8}$	$\frac{9}{16}$	$\frac{1}{4}$	$\frac{7}{16}$	$\frac{1}{2}$

Repeat for this set of eight fractions.

$\frac{1}{6}$	$\frac{5}{12}$	$\frac{6}{8}$	$\frac{7}{12}$	$\frac{2}{3}$	$\frac{5}{6}$	$\frac{11}{12}$	$\frac{1}{3}$

Try to put all 16 fractions into order.

Name ....

Ordering mixed numbers

for 2 children

$\frac{36}{10}$	$\frac{9}{4}$	$5\frac{1}{2}$	$\frac{23}{7}$	$2\frac{9}{10}$	$7\frac{2}{3}$	$\frac{28}{6}$	$4\frac{3}{4}$	$\frac{31}{9}$	$3\frac{7}{8}$

Look at the list of improper fractions and mixed numbers. Without changing any of them to a different form, write them in the order you think they should go in, from smallest to largest. Then convert the improper fractions to mixed numbers. Write the 10 mixed numbers in order, smallest to largest. Compare this to your estimated order. Were you right?

Equivalent fractions

for 2 children

Each write three sets of equivalent decimals and fractions. Swap with your partner and check each other's answers.

For example: $\dfrac{3}{10} = \dfrac{30}{100} = 0.3$

Write 10 fractions between 0 and $\frac{1}{2}$. Work together to arrange these fractions in order from smallest to largest. Use a calculator to find each fraction as a decimal by dividing the numerator by the denominator. Write the decimals in order from smallest to largest and compare this order with your original fraction order. Were you right?

Abacus Evolve Framework Edition Year 5 PCM © Harcourt Education Ltd 2007

Equivalent fractions

for 2 children

Make a pair of equivalent fractions using four of the numbers 1–20. You must not use a number twice.

$$\dfrac{\boxed{3}}{\boxed{4}} = \dfrac{12}{16} \qquad \dfrac{\boxed{1}}{\boxed{2}} \not= \dfrac{2}{4}$$

Make a second pair of equivalent fractions using JUST these numbers. Can you make a third pair? A fourth pair?
How many pairs of equivalent fractions do you think can be made from the numbers 1–20? Be prepared to give reasons for your guess.

Abacus Evolve Framework Edition Year 5 PCM © Harcourt Education Ltd 2007

Name _____

Equivalent fractions

for 1 or 2 children

Use the multiplication square to write pairs of equivalent fractions.
One fraction of the pair must have a numerator of 6.

For example: $\dfrac{6}{10} = \dfrac{3}{5}$

Repeat for pairs of which one fraction has a denominator of 6.

For example: $\dfrac{3}{6} = \dfrac{1}{2}$

Try this with a different number, for example 10.

1	2	3	4	5	6	7	8	9	10
2	4	6	8	10	12	14	16	18	20
3	6	9	12	15	18	21	24	27	30
4	8	12	16	20	24	28	32	36	40
5	10	15	20	25	30	35	40	45	50
6	12	18	24	30	36	42	48	54	60
7	14	21	28	35	42	49	56	63	70
8	16	24	32	40	48	56	64	72	80
9	18	27	36	45	54	63	72	81	90
10	20	30	40	50	60	70	80	90	100

Name _____

Ordering fractions

for 3 or 4 children

You need fraction cards: $\frac{1}{2}$, $\frac{1}{3}$, $\frac{2}{3}$, $\frac{1}{4}$, $\frac{3}{4}$, $\frac{1}{6}$, $\frac{5}{6}$, $\frac{1}{8}$, $\frac{3}{8}$, $\frac{5}{8}$, $\frac{7}{8}$.

Select one fraction card each. Your aim is to place all your fractions in order, smallest to largest. Work together to put the cards into what you think is the right order. Everyone must now convert their own fraction into an equivalent number of 24ths. Compare your fractions, and check if the order was correct. Write all the fractions and their equivalents in 24ths in order. Replace the cards and repeat this at least six times.

$\dfrac{1}{3}$ $\dfrac{2}{3}$ $\dfrac{1}{6}$ $\dfrac{3}{8}$ $\dfrac{5}{8}$

$\dfrac{1}{2}$ $\dfrac{1}{4}$ $\dfrac{3}{4}$ $\dfrac{5}{6}$ $\dfrac{1}{8}$ $\dfrac{7}{8}$

Abacus Evolve Framework Edition Year 5 PCM © Harcourt Education Ltd 2007

Abacus Evolve Framework Edition Year 5 PCM © Harcourt Education Ltd 2007

Three in a line

for 2 children

You need number cards 0–9 and a set of counters for each player in their own colour. Shuffle the cards and deal four to each player to make a 4-digit number. Each player rounds their number to the nearest 1000, and covers the answer on the grid with a counter, unless the number is already covered. Reshuffle the cards and repeat.
The winner is the first to get three counters in a straight line.

4000	9000	2000
1000	5000	8000
7000	3000	6000

Invent a similar game for rounding to the nearest 100.

Abacus Evolve Framework Edition Year 5 PCM © Harcourt Education Ltd 2007

Approximate and actual answers

for 2 children

You need number cards 0–9.
Select five number cards to create a 3-digit number and a 2-digit number. Round the 3-digit number to the nearest 100, and the 2-digit number to the nearest 10. Multiply the two rounded numbers together. Write the multiplication and the answer. Now use a calculator to multiply the original two numbers together, and write the multiplication and answer. Work out the difference between the approximate and actual answers.
Have another go, this time trying to make a multiplication for which the actual answer is as close as possible to the approximated answer.
Repeat several times. How close can you make the two answers?

$$\boxed{5}\ \boxed{4}\ \boxed{7}\ \times\ \boxed{2}\ \boxed{9}$$

$$500 \times 30 = 15\,000$$
$$547 \times 29 = 15\,863$$

$$15\,863 - 15\,000 = 863$$

Ordering decimals

for 3 or 4 children

You need units, tenths and hundredths place-value cards. Shuffle each set of cards and place them face down in three piles. Select one from each pile to create a decimal number, for example 7·35. Repeat eight times so that you have nine decimal numbers.

Arrange them in order, smallest to largest.

Find the difference between the first two numbers. Find the difference between the second and third numbers, then the third and fourth, and so on. Which pair has the largest difference, and which the smallest?

Reshuffle the cards and repeat.

Kilograms and grams

for 2 children

Write two weights in kilograms with two decimal places. They should be quite close to each other. Each of you then converts the weights to grams.

4·35 kg	4·67 kg
4350 g	4670 g

Together, choose a weight in grams between the two.
Then convert this weight to kilograms.

4490 g
4·49 kg

Do this 10 times, starting with two different weights in kilograms each time.

Abacus Evolve Framework Edition Year 5 PCM © Harcourt Education Ltd 2007

Dividing by 10 and 100

for 2 or 3 children

Cover each number on the grid with a counter. Take turns to remove a counter to reveal a number, for example 4700. Divide the number by 10, and say the answer in words, for example *four hundred and seventy*. If correct, keep the counter. If not, replace it. When all the counters have been removed, the winner is the player with the most counters.

14 600	4200	700	17 300	1100	4700	25 400	100
2300	20 800	9400	3100	36 800	800	5600	70 400
61 900	600	8300	51 200	900	7500	41 300	1900

Repeat the game, but this time divide the numbers by 100.

Abacus Evolve Framework Edition Year 5 PCM © Harcourt Education Ltd 2007

Close to £100

for 3 children

You need number cards 0–9.
Shuffle the cards and deal out nine. Use these numbers to create three amounts of money, for example £175, £328 and £469. Choose one of these amounts each. Divide your amount by 10 and record your divisions. Round your answer to the nearest pound. Write an addition for the three new amounts, and complete it. How close to £100 is the total?
Repeat this at least five times. How close to £100 can you get?

$£175 ÷ 10 = £17·50$ $£17·50 → £18$

$£18 + £33 + £47 = £98$

Name ....

Common multiples   **for 3 children**

> You need number cards 2–II and some cubes.
> Shuffle the cards and place them face down in a pile. One of you takes two cards, and says a common multiple of the two card numbers. If you are correct, collect a cube. Record the two card numbers and the common multiple, then replace the cards and reshuffle the pack. The other two players then take turns to do the same thing. When it is your turn, you cannot say a common multiple that has already been said!
> Have several turns each.

| 2 | 7 | 2, 7 $\longrightarrow$ 28

Name ....

Smallest common multiples   **for 3 or 4 children**

> You need number cards 2–9 and some counters. Deal two cards. Each write the smallest common multiple of these two numbers. Check each other's answers. If correct, collect a counter. Repeat for several rounds.

| 4 | 6 | smallest common multiple = I2

> Extend the activity by dealing three cards, and finding the smallest common multiple of all three.

Abacus Evolve Framework Edition Year 5 PCM © Harcourt Education Ltd 2007

Name ....

Multiplying

for 2 children

You need number cards 15–100 (multiples of 5 only) and a dice with the 1 changed to a 7.
Shuffle the cards and place them face down in a pile. Take a card each.
Take turns to throw the dice. Write a multiplication for the two numbers.
Draw a rectangle each to help you to multiply.

 × 45

	40	5
4		

Both fill in the two boxes in your rectangle, then add the two numbers. Compare your answers, and check using a calculator by dividing your answer by the dice number. If the answer is the card number, your multiplication is correct!
Repeat the activity, taking a new card each.
Try generating some more multiplications using the same number cards, but make up your own multipliers, larger than the dice numbers.

Name ....

Good estimating

for 3 children

You will need a set of number cards 0–9. Shuffle them and deal three to each person to create a 2-digit number and a 1-digit number, which must then be multiplied together. Each person draws a table and writes their multiplication in the first column. Then write an estimate, before finding the actual answer. Check each other's multiplications. Finally, each person writes the difference between their estimate and their answer.

Multiplication	Estimate	Answer	Difference
3 × 76	240	228	12

Play six rounds, then find each person's total difference. The winner is the one with the smallest total.

Abacus Evolve Framework Edition Year 5 PCM © Harcourt Education Ltd 2007

Multiplying by doubling

for 2–4 children

Multiply the numbers at the top of the grid by the numbers to the right.
Use these methods:
(1) **16**: multiply by 8, then double
(2) **14**: multiply by 7, then double
(3) **24**: multiply by 6, then double and double again
(4) **36**: multiply by 9, then double and double again.

7	9	6	8	
				× 16
				× 14
				× 24
				× 36

Which multiplications give the same answers? Can you explain why?

Dividing by 4

for 2 children

You need a dice.
Take turns to throw the dice four times to create your own 4-digit even number. If you cannot make an even number with your dice numbers, throw the dice again until you can. Each divide the dice number by 4, by halving twice. If the answer is not a whole number, write it as a decimal. If you are able, halve the number again. Check each other's answers using a calculator: multiply the answer by 4 (or 8 if you halved three times) – the answer should be the 4-digit number you started with!
Do this eight times.

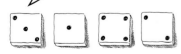

$3142 \div 2 = 1571$ $1571 \div 2 = 785 \cdot 5$

check: $785 \cdot 5 \times 4 = 3142$

Abacus Evolve Framework Edition Year 5 PCM © Harcourt Education Ltd 2007

Abacus Evolve Framework Edition Year 5 PCM © Harcourt Education Ltd 2007

Abacus Evolve Framework Edition Year 5 PCM © Harcourt Education Ltd 2007

Coordinates island

for 2 children

You need two sheets of squared paper, each with a 10 × 10 grid drawn on. Take a grid each. This is going to be your coordinate grid. Number the horizontal axis 0–10 and the vertical axis 0–10. Then, draw an island on your grid, and draw various features on the island and in the sea, such as palm trees, a house, a shark, a boat. You must draw them at points where two lines cross.

Now you can play the game! One of you says a pair of coordinates. The other person finds that spot on their grid. If there is a feature in that position, you must tell your partner, who makes a note of which feature they have 'visited'. Keep taking turns to do this, until one player has visited all the features on their partner's map!

Abacus Evolve Framework Edition Year 5 PCM © Harcourt Education Ltd 2007

Capital letters

for 3 or 4 children

You need some 6 × 6 coordinate grids.
The capital letter 'H' can be made by joining these points:
(1, 5) to (1, 1)
(1, 3) to (4, 3)
(4, 5) to (4, 1)
Describe to each other ways of joining points to make other capital letters. Write them down.

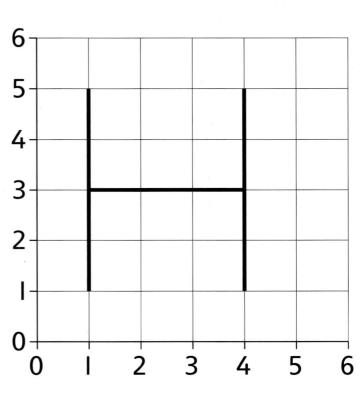

Shape overlaps

for 2 or 3 children

> You need several pieces of tracing paper. Cut out two equal-sized squares of tracing paper. Place one partly over the other so that they overlap. Look at the shape made by the overlap. What shape is it?
> Investigate different overlapping shapes, and their names.
> Make a display, labelling the different overlap shapes.

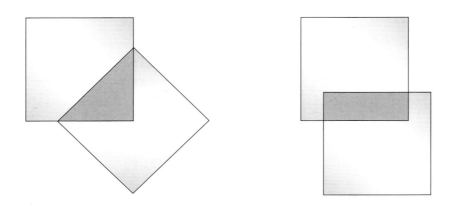

Hole shapes

for 2 children

> You need two pieces of paper and a pair of scissors.
> Take a piece of paper each and fold it in half twice. Cut three straight lines around the corner. Draw and name the shape that you think the hole will be when you open the paper out! Then, watch each other open your papers, and check what the actual shapes are. Draw your actual shape next to your estimated shape and write its name. Draw the lines of symmetry. Repeat this several times. In all the shapes, how many lines of symmetry did you find?

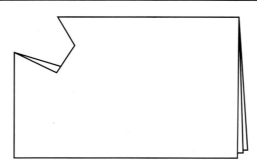

Abacus Evolve Framework Edition Year 5 PCM © Harcourt Education Ltd 2007

Shape areas

for 2 children

You need two sheets of squared paper.
Take a sheet of squared paper each. Each draw a simple irregular polygon. It must be different from your partner's! Swap shapes, and work out the area of each other's shape by counting the squares. Only count squares that are a half or larger. Ignore any that are less than a half! Write the area in squares. Then swap back and check each other's work. Do you agree with your partner?
Repeat the activity, drawing a new shape for each other to work out the area. Can you draw one where it is possible to calculate the area, rather than counting the squares?

Areas of rectangles

for 2 or 3 children

Draw five different rectangles. Calculate their areas.
For each rectangle, draw another rectangle whose sides are double these. Calculate their areas. Look for patterns in the areas of each pair of rectangles. Describe the pattern.

5 cm

3 cm

10 cm

6 cm

$3 \text{cm} \times 5 \text{cm} = 15 \text{cm}^2$
$6 \text{cm} \times 10 \text{cm} =$

Repeat the activity, but instead of doubling the lengths, treble them.

Abacus Evolve Framework Edition Year 5 PCM © Harcourt Education Ltd 2007

Name ....

Perimeter patterns

for 2 children

You need two sheets of squared paper.
Take a sheet of squared paper each. One of you must draw a 4 × 6 rectangle, and the other must draw a 5 × 7 rectangle. Work out the perimeter of your own rectangle, and write it beside it.
Draw a new rectangle each: one 6 × 8, and the other 7 × 9. Work out their perimeters and write them down. Draw a table like this to record your results:

Rectangle	4 × 6	5 × 7	6 × 8	7 × 9	8 × 10	9 × 11	10 × 12
Perimeter							

Keep drawing rectangles, increasing the length and width by one unit each time. Write all the perimeters in your table. What patterns can you see?
Repeat the activity, starting with a different sized rectangle and increasing the length and width in the same way. Is the pattern the same?

Name ....

Perimeters of rectangles

for 3 or 4 children

8 cm

2 cm

4 cm

6 cm

7 cm

3 cm

Here are three rectangles, each with a perimeter of 20 cm. Calculate their areas. Are they the same?
Draw three different rectangles, each with a perimeter of 32 cm. Calculate their areas.
Investigate which rectangle with a perimeter of 80 cm has the largest area.

Abacus Evolve Framework Edition Year 5 PCM © Harcourt Education Ltd 2007

Name ....

Days between birthdays

for 4 children

Each write down your birthday. Write how many days there are in each month of the year. Calculate exactly how many days there are between your birthday and the birthday of every other person in the group. Show all your workings. Check the numbers of days with the rest of the group to see if you all agree.

23rd March

16th August

30th December

9th July

Name ....

Minutes in class

for 2 children

Work out the number of minutes you spend in class every week! First of all, work out how many hours this is. Remember – don't include break time or lunch!

Abacus Evolve Framework Edition Year 5 PCM © Harcourt Education Ltd 2007

Abacus Evolve Framework Edition Year 5 PCM © Harcourt Education Ltd 2007

Name ....

Inventing train timetables

for 2 children

Copy out this train timetable:

	Train A	Train B	Train C	Train D
Boreton	11·27			
Carwick	12·34			
Bogsea	12·58			
Whitton	13·46			
Bumptown	14·12			
Popville	14·49			

Invent start times for Trains B, C and D, and write them in the first row. Complete the timetable, assuming that each train takes the same time between stations as Train A.

Name ....

Palindromes

for 3 or 4 children

A palindrome is a word or number that is the same when you write it backwards as when you write it forwards. For example:

nun

484

mum

Hannah

madam

12321

redder

You are going to write some 24-hour times that are palindromes – for example 15:51. Work together to write down as many as you can. Can you work out exactly how many palindromic times there are in 24 hours?

Abacus Evolve Framework Edition Year 5 PCM © Harcourt Education Ltd 2007

Flower values

for 3 or 4 children

Each letter of the alphabet has been given a value.

a	b	c	d	e	f	g	h	i	j	k	l	m
30	60	70	90	40	10	50	90	30	60	20	50	70

n	o	p	q	r	s	t	u	v	w	x	y	z
50	40	20	80	50	40	60	40	60	50	80	10	40

The total value of the word 'tulip' is 200.
Find the total value of six other flowers.

t   u   l   i   p
60 + 40 + 50 + 30 + 20 = 200

Choose your own topic, for example colours, and find the value of some different words.

Abacus Evolve Framework Edition Year 5 PCM © Harcourt Education Ltd 2007

Multiples of 100

for 2 children

You need number cards 10–120 (multiples of 10) and a dice.
Spread the cards out face up. Take a turn each to throw the dice. Multiply your dice number by 100, to make a multiple of 100. Then you must find card numbers that add up to that number. Try to find more than one way of doing it!
Are some multiples of 100 harder to make than others?

   $4 \times 100 = 400$

$10 + 20 + 30 + 40 + 50 + 60 + 90 + 100 = 400$

Adding 2-digit numbers

for 3 children

You need tens and units place-value cards.
Shuffle the cards and place them face down in two piles. Each of you takes a card from each pile, so that you all have a 2-digit number. Write the three 2-digit numbers as an addition. One of you adds the tens. One of you adds the units. One of you adds the tens and units together. Complete the addition together.
Do this 10 times, reshuffling the cards in between.

| 2 | 5 |

| 7 | 4 |

25 + 74 + 36

| 3 | 6 |

20 + 70 + 30 = 120
5 + 4 + 6 = 15
120 + 15 = 135

25 + 74 + 36 = 135

Adding 3-digit numbers

for 4 children

For this activity, work in two pairs.
You need hundreds, tens and units place-value cards. Shuffle the three sets of cards and deal out one of each type to each pair. Use your three cards to create a 3-digit number. Working in your pairs, add the two numbers together.

Now you can check your answers!
Place both hundreds cards together, and add them.
Place both tens cards together and add them.
Place both units cards together and add them.
Finally, add these three totals together, and check that this matches your answers.
Shuffle the cards and repeat several times.

| 3 | 7 | 2 |

| 4 | 6 | 5 |

| 300 |

| 400 |

| 70 |

| 60 |

| 2 |

| 5 |

Name _____

Adding near multiples of 10   for 3 or 4 children

You need hundreds, tens and units place-value cards, a dice and a small pile of 1p coins. Shuffle the three sets of cards and deal out one of each type to each person. Use your three cards to create a 3-digit number. Roll the dice to find out what you have to add to or subtract from your number. These are what the dice numbers stand for:

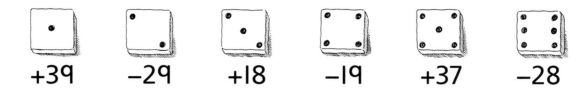

+39   −29   +18   −19   +37   −28

Write your calculation, for example 362 + 37 = 399. Check each other's calculations. Players with correct answers collect 1p coins to match the units digit of their answer (for example, if the answer was 399, you would collect 9p). Play several rounds. Who collects the most money?

Abacus Evolve Framework Edition Year 5 PCM © Harcourt Education Ltd 2007

Name _____

Reverse numbers   for 2 children

Choose a 3-digit number with consecutive digits. Reverse the digits to make a second 3-digit number. Add the two numbers by partitioning.
Repeat, starting with a different 3-digit number. Do this several times. What patterns do you notice?

123 ⟶ 321   123 + 321 =

Try starting with two different 3-digit numbers with consecutive digits. Reverse both of them. Add the four numbers together. For example 123 + 321 + 456 + 654.

Try finding the differences between 3-digit numbers with consecutive digits and their reverses. For example 654 − 456.

Abacus Evolve Framework Edition Year 5 PCM © Harcourt Education Ltd 2007

Decimal bingo

for 3 or 4 children

You need number cards 0–9 and a bingo board each.
Shuffle the number cards and place them face down in a pile. Each write five 1-place decimal numbers between 0 and 1 on your bingo board. Take two cards each and use the numbers to create a 1-place decimal number. You can place the numbers either way round. Work out how much must be added to reach the next whole number. Anyone with that number written on their bingo board may cross it out. Continue like this until one person has crossed out all the numbers on their board.
Start with a new board each and play again!

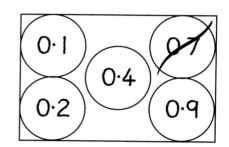

$$\boxed{4} \cdot \boxed{3} \quad 4.3 + 0.7 = 5$$

Making the next whole number

for 3 or 4 children

You need units, tenths and hundredths place value cards and a calculator. Shuffle the cards and deal them out to create nine decimal numbers. Write them down, and then work out what must be added to each to make the next whole number.
Use a calculator to add together all of the numbers you added on.
Reshuffle the cards and repeat the activity. Are the two answers the same? Can you explain this?

$$\boxed{1 \cdot 2\ 7} + 0.73 = 2.00$$

$$\boxed{5 \cdot 3\ 6} + 0.64 = 6.00$$

...   .
_____

Total: _____

Abacus Evolve Framework Edition Year 5 PCM © Harcourt Education Ltd 2007

Multiplying by 5

for 3 children

You need hundreds, tens and units place-value cards.
Shuffle the cards and place them face down in their sets. Choose a set each, and take one card from your pile. Combine your number with the other numbers to create one 3-digit number, which you should all write down. Multiply your own card number by 5, and record the calculation. Then add the three parts together and write the complete multiplication of the 3-digit number by 5.

$$\boxed{3 \mid 6 \mid 2}\!\!>$$

$5 \times 300 = 1500$ $5 \times 60 = 300$ $5 \times 2 = 10$

$1500 + 300 + 10 = 1810$

$5 \times 362 = 1810$

Abacus Evolve Framework Edition Year 5 PCM © Harcourt Education Ltd 2007

Ordering multiplications

for 4 children

This game is for four people, playing in pairs.
You need hundreds, tens and units place-value cards, and number cards 2–9. Shuffle each set of cards and deal out one of each type to create a 3-digit number and a 1-digit number. You will multiply these together.

$$\boxed{600}\!\!> \quad \boxed{40}\!\!> \quad \boxed{7}\!\!> \qquad \boxed{5}$$

647×5

Repeat five more times to create six multiplications. Each pair writes the multiplications in order of how large they think the answers will be, from largest to smallest. Both pairs then work together to find the actual answers. When all the multiplications have been completed, compare the correct order with the estimated order.

Name

Multiplying 2-digit numbers   for 2 children

You need number cards 30–80 and cubes.
Shuffle the number cards and place them face down in a pile. Take two cards each. Write a multiplication using your two numbers. Estimate the answer, and write down your estimate. Perform the multiplications, using whichever method you like. Then, check each other's answers using a calculator to divide the total by one of the card numbers – if the answer is the other card number, your multiplication was correct! Compare the actual answer with your estimate. Which of you was closest? That person collects a cube!

$$44 \times 57$$

Estimate: $40 \times 60 = 2400$

$$
\begin{array}{r}
44 \\
\times\ 57 \\
\hline
308 \\
2200 \\
\hline
2508 \\
\end{array}
$$

44×7
44×50

Name

Digit swap   for 2 or 3 children

Multiply 39×62. Swap the digits round, 93×26, and multiply again.
What do you notice?
Repeat for 46×32 and 64×23.
Can you find more pairs like this? Can you explain your findings and predict which multiplications will give answers like this?

$$
\begin{array}{r}
39 \\
\times\ 62 \\
\hline
\end{array}
$$

39×2

39×60

Guess my calculation

for 3 or 4 children

$\frac{1}{4}$	$\frac{7}{10}$	$\frac{1}{2}$
$\frac{2}{3}$	$\frac{1}{5}$	$\frac{3}{4}$
$\frac{1}{8}$	$\frac{3}{5}$	$\frac{1}{3}$

£80	£36	£50
£32	£60	£40
£90	£70	£24

Take turns to secretly choose a fraction from the left-hand grid and an amount from the right-hand grid. Work out that fraction of the amount. Say the answer. The other children have to guess which fraction and amount you chose. How many guesses do they take? Have several turns each.

Ages

for 2 children

Maud was born on 17th October 1934. Work together to work out Maud's age to the nearest month as a mixed number.

Work together to find out how many days there are in one-tenth of a year. Give your answer to the nearest day!

Write your own age as a mixed number using tenths. Then write it as a decimal number!

Abacus Evolve Framework Edition Year 5 PCM © Harcourt Education Ltd 2007

Divisibility

for 3 or 4 children

You need number cards 0–9.
Use the cards to create numbers that are divisible by 2.
Start by creating as many 1-digit numbers as you can.
Next create as many 2-digit numbers as you can.
Extend to 3-digit and 4-digit numbers.

8

9 4

7 5 2

Repeat the activity for numbers that are divisible by 5, then 4, and then 3.

Dividing by 3, 6 and 9

for 3 children

Which of these numbers can be divided by 3? Which can be divided by 6?
Which can be divided by 9? Make three lists.

27   72   12   63

29   18   30

48   16

54   50   81

Is there an easy way to tell if a number can be divided by 3? What about numbers that can be divided by 6? Numbers that can be divided by 9? Can you write rules for these?

Abacus Evolve Framework Edition Year 5 PCM © Harcourt Education Ltd 2007

Ordering positive and negative numbers   for 2 children

You need integer cards ⁻10 to ⁺10, and five blank cards.
Place the blank cards in a row to represent the positions of five numbers in order from smallest to largest. Shuffle the integer cards and place them face down in a pile. Player A turns over one card, and places it on top of one of the blank cards. The aim is to try to get all five numbers in order. Once a card has been placed, it cannot be moved! Player A takes another card, and places it. Continue until five numbers are placed in the row. If they are in the correct order, score 5 points.
Remove the five cards, shuffle them into the pack, and then Player B has a turn.
Play several rounds.

| ⁻7 | ⁻3 | ⁻1 | ⁺4 | ⁺9 |

Abacus Evolve Framework Edition Year 5 PCM © Harcourt Education Ltd 2007

Positive and negative number grid   for 2 children

You need number cards 0–10, and a counter and 20 cubes each.
Draw a large 4 × 4 grid. Write a different number in each box in the grid. Use a mixture of positive and negative numbers, between ⁻12 and ⁺12. Each of you places your counter on any number on the grid. Shuffle the number cards and place them face down in a pile.
One of you goes first. Move your counter one square up, down, left or right. Pick up a number card. You must choose whether to add or subtract the card number from the grid number your counter is on. The aim is to get a score as close to 0 as possible! Work out the difference between your score and 0, and give your partner that number of cubes. For example, if your score is ⁻2, you must give your partner 2 cubes. Replace the number card on the bottom of the pile.
Take turns to do this until one of you loses all your cubes!

Rounding decimals

for 2 children

Use number cards 0–9.
Shuffle the cards and spread them out face down. Take three cards each, and use them to make a decimal number with two decimal places. Check each other's number, round your number to the nearest whole number and write it down. Score points to match the whole number that your decimal rounded to.
Replace the cards, shuffle them around, and take three new cards each.
Repeat the activity.
Continue playing like this until one of you has scored 50 points!

| 5 | · | 3 | 1 |

5

score: 5 points

| 2 | · | 6 | 0 |

3

score: 3 points

Rounding decimals

for 2 or 3 children

Use number cards 0–9.
Shuffle the cards and deal out five. Use them to create different decimal numbers with two decimal places. Investigate how many you can make that round to 1 when you round to the nearest whole number.

How many decimal numbers can you make, using the same set of five cards, that round to 2? to 3? to 4?

Name _____

Abacus Evolve Framework Edition Year 5 PCM © Harcourt Education Ltd 2007

Multiplying dice game   **for 3 or 4 children**

You need number cards 20–50 and a dice.
Shuffle the cards and reveal one at random, for example 26.
Each person rolls the dice to see what to multiply the card number by:

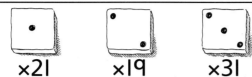

×21   ×19   ×31   ×29   ×22   ×18

Each work out your multiplication, showing your workings.

$26 \times 20 = 520$
$26 \times 21 = 520 + 26 = 546$

Check each other's answers. If you got it right, score points to match the units digit of your answer. (If your answer was 546, you would score 6 points.)
Play several rounds. Who has scored the most points?

Name _____

Abacus Evolve Framework Edition Year 5 PCM © Harcourt Education Ltd 2007

Multiplying by 99   **for 2 children**

You need number cards 31–79, with the multiples of 10 removed.
Shuffle the cards. Take a card each. Multiply your number by 99, by multiplying by 100, and then subtracting the card number. Check each other's answers using a calculator: divide the number by 99, and if the answer is the card number, then the calculation was correct!

$\boxed{37}$ $\times 99 = (37 \times 100) - 37 = 3700 - 37 = 3663$

Now work out the digital root of your answer by adding the digits together until you get a single-digit total.
Repeat this activity until you have done at least six calculations each. What do you notice about the digital roots?

$3 + 6 + 6 + 3 = 18$ $1 + 8 = 9$ the digital root is 9

Multiplying decimal numbers   **for 3 children**

You need number cards 1–9.
Shuffle the cards and spread them out face down. Take two cards each.
Each arrange your cards to make a decimal number with one decimal place.
Write a multiplication to multiply your decimal number by 5. Draw a
rectangle to perform your multiplication. Fill in the two boxes, and then add
the two parts to find the total. Check each other's work by using a calculator
to divide the answers by 5. You should return to the original number!
Replace the cards, shuffle them around and repeat the activity several times.

$$\boxed{3} \cdot \boxed{6} \qquad 5 \times 3\cdot6$$

	3	0·6	
5	15	3·0	15 + 3·0 = 18

Try the same activity, but this time multiply your decimal numbers by 4.

Eight multiplications   **for 4 children**

You need units and tenths place value-cards, and number cards 2–9.
Shuffle the place-value cards and deal out eight from each set to create
eight decimal numbers. Shuffle the number cards and deal out eight, one to
go with each decimal number. These are the multipliers. Work in pairs to
multiply each decimal number by the number on the card. Don't let the
other pair see your answers! When you've all finished, compare answers.
Check together any calculations for which your answers don't match. Score
1 point for each correct answer. How many points did you score?
Reshuffle the cards, and repeat.

$$\boxed{4 \mid \cdot 7} \times \boxed{3} = 14\cdot1$$

Abacus Evolve Framework Edition Year 5 PCM © Harcourt Education Ltd 2007

Adding 4-digit numbers   **for 4 children**

You need thousands, hundreds, tens and units place-value cards.
Shuffle the cards, then select two of each type to create two 4-digit
numbers. Work in two pairs. Each pair adds the two numbers together,
without letting the other pair see their working. Then both pairs check
their answers together. You can use a calculator to check if you wish. If
your answer was correct, your pair collects 5 points.
Reshuffle the cards and repeat. Play several rounds. Which pair collects
more points?

| 2 | 5 | 7 | 3 |

| 4 | 1 | 9 | 6 |

$$
\begin{array}{r}
2573 \\
+\ 4196 \\
\hline
\\
\hline
\end{array}
$$

Abacus Evolve Framework Edition Year 5 PCM © Harcourt Education Ltd 2007

Digital roots of additions   **for 2 children**

Write an addition of two 4-digit numbers, and calculate the answer.
Work out the digital root of each of the numbers you added.
Add these two digital roots together.
Work out the digital root of the answer to the addition. What do you notice?
Try this with some other additions. Can you see a pattern?

$$
\begin{array}{r}
4683 \\
+\ 5279 \\
\hline
9962 \\
\end{array}
$$
1 1

$4 + 6 + 8 + 3 = 21$ $2 + 1 = 3$
$5 + 2 + 7 + 9 = 23$ $2 + 3 = 5$
                             $3 + 5 = 8$
$9 + 9 + 6 + 2 = 26$ $2 + 6 =$

Name ....

Close to £9

for 2 children

You need a set of number cards 1–9 each, and six cubes.
Spread the cards out face up. Each of you should use all nine numbers to create an addition of three amounts in pounds and pence. Write your addition, and then calculate the answer.
When you have both finished, compare totals. Whoever's total is nearest to £9 collects a cube.
Repeat this activity six times. Who collected more cubes? Who had the total closest to £9?

$$
\begin{array}{r}
5{\cdot}86 \\
3{\cdot}14 \\
+\ 2{\cdot}79 \\
\hline
£11{\cdot}79 \\
\end{array}
$$
        1 1

Name ....

Close to 10

for 2 or 3 children

You need number cards 0–9.
Use the cards to create three decimal numbers, each with two decimal places. Add them together.
Investigate ways of choosing three numbers so that they have a total as close to 10 as possible.

| 5 | · | 8 | 6 | | 3 | · | 1 | 7 | | 2 | · | 0 | 9 |

$$
\begin{array}{r}
5{\cdot}86 \\
3{\cdot}17 \\
+2{\cdot}09 \\
\hline

\end{array}
$$

Abacus Evolve Framework Edition Year 5 PCM © Harcourt Education Ltd 2007

Subtraction investigation   for 3 or 4 children

You need number cards 2–8.
Use the cards to create a 4-digit number and a 3-digit number.
Subtract the smaller number from the larger.

5	3	7	6
−	8	2	9

Investigate subtractions that have an answer close to 2000... 3000... 4000... 5000...

Abacus Evolve Framework Edition Year 5 PCM © Harcourt Education Ltd 2007

Subtracting reversed numbers   for 2 children

Write a 3-digit number with consecutive digits.
Reverse the number, and write it down.
Subtract the smaller number from the larger.
Repeat this several times.

123   321

$$\begin{array}{r} 321 \\ -123 \\ \hline \end{array}$$

Write a 4-digit number, reverse it, and subtract the smaller number from the larger.
What patterns have you noticed?

Name ....

Subtracting money amounts

for 2 children

You need £1, 10p and 1p coins.
Choose an amount in pounds and pence. Make this amount using £1, 10p and 1p coins. Write a second amount, smaller than the first, but with more 1ps. You will subtract the second amount from the first one. Decide who will subtract the 1ps, and who will subtract the 10ps. The 10p person will have to give one 10p coin to the 1p person. Work together to subtract the pounds.
Record the subtraction and the answer. Check using a calculator: add your answer to the smaller amount. You should get the larger amount! Repeat this five times.

£5·73 − £3·48

13p − 8p

60p − 40p

£5 − £3

Name ....

Decimal differences

for 4 children

You need units, tenths and hundredths place-value cards.
Each of you selects one of each type of card to create a decimal number with two decimal places. Work out the difference between your number and each of the other people's numbers. Check each other's answers to see if they match. Use a calculator if you are unsure who is right! For each correct answer, collect 1 point. Reshuffle the cards and play several more rounds.

$4 \cdot 3 \ 2$ $3 \cdot 6 \ 7$ $8 \cdot 0 \ 9$ $6 \cdot 7 \ 1$

$$6 \cdot 7 \ 1$$
$$- 4 \cdot 3 \ 2$$
$$\overline{}$$

$$8 \cdot 0 \ 9$$
$$- 4 \cdot 3 \ 2$$
$$\overline{}$$

$$4 \cdot 3 \ 2$$
$$- 3 \cdot 6 \ 7$$
$$\overline{}$$

Abacus Evolve Framework Edition Year 5 PCM © Harcourt Education Ltd 2007

Name _____

Abacus Evolve Framework Edition Year 5 PCM © Harcourt Education Ltd 2007

Likely or unlikely?

for 4 children

You need 16 blank cards or pieces of paper. Work in pairs. Each pair writes:
- two events that are 'likely' to happen tonight
- two events that are 'unlikely' to happen tonight
- two events that are 'impossible' to happen tonight
- two events that are 'certain' to happen tonight.

Arrange the 16 cards in a line, in order of how likely they are to happen, with the least likely on the left and the most likely on the right.

| Tonight I will sleep. | Tonight I will read a book. | Tonight I will go to Spain. |

Name _____

Abacus Evolve Framework Edition Year 5 PCM © Harcourt Education Ltd 2007

Playing card possibilities

for 2 children

You need a pack of playing cards without the picture cards and card labels with these headings:

| No chance | Poor chance | Even chance | Good chance | Certain |

Work together to write events involving the shuffled pack of playing cards under each heading. Try different actions with the cards, and make sure they are under the most suitable heading.

| Certain | If I reveal one card, it will be either red or black. |

| Poor chance | If I reveal one card, it will be more than 8. |

Name

Creating a graph

for 2 children

Invent and draw a line graph to show the changes in temperature from 6 o'clock in the morning to 8 o'clock at night.
Write a description to explain the graph.

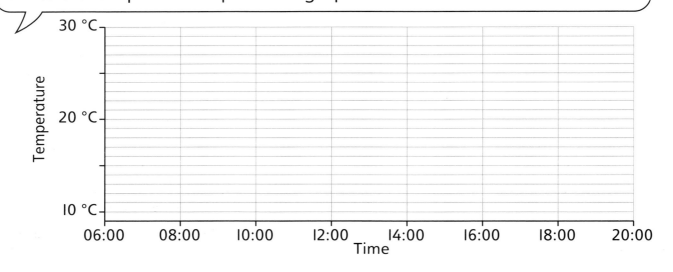

Name

Water challenge

for 4 children

You need a litre measure marked in millimetres, a stopwatch and a water tap. Choose one job each: timing, controlling the tap, reading measurements or recording. Start the timer and set the tap dripping or running very gently into the measure.
After 1 minute, the timer calls 'time', and the reader calls out how many millimetres of water are in the measure for the recorder to write down. At the same time the tap controller should change the dripping speed (either slightly faster or slightly slower).
Repeat this every minute for 6 minutes and record your measurements in the table below.

Time in minutes	1	2	3	4	5	6
Amount in millimetres						

Each draw a line graph to show your findings, with the time in minutes placed horizontally and the amount in millimetres placed vertically.
Discuss the graphs. When was the tap dripping at its fastest?

Capacity game

for 2 children

Capacity:

| 1 l | 2 l | 600 ml | 3 l | $\frac{1}{2}$ l | 5 l |

Fraction:

| $\frac{1}{2}$ | $\frac{1}{4}$ | $\frac{3}{4}$ | $\frac{1}{10}$ | $\frac{1}{100}$ | $\frac{1}{5}$ |

You need a six-sided dice.
One of you rolls the dice to decide a capacity. The other rolls the dice to decide a fraction. For example, if you roll a 4 and then a 6, you will need to work out $\frac{1}{5}$ of 3 litres. Discuss between you what the fraction of the capacity is in millilitres, and write it down.
Do this 10 times.

Drinks

for 2 children

Work together to calculate how much you each drink in a week.
Start by going through a typical school day for each of you. How much do you drink at breakfast time? At break time? At lunch time? After school? At dinner time? Before bed? Record the amounts in millilitres or fractions of a litre. Add them together to find an average daily amount in millilitres. Multiply this amount by 5 to find out how much you drink during the week. Then think about the weekend – do you drink more or less than on weekdays? Work out a total amount for an average weekend day, and then multiply it by 2 to find the total for a whole weekend.
Add the weekday and weekend amounts together. Write the total in litres and millilitres.
Now, convert this amount to pints!

Name ....

Angle-maker

for 2 children

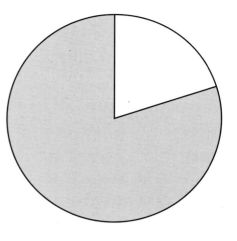

Cut out two equal-sized paper circles of different colours. Find the centre of each circle by folding them in half, and half again, then opening out. Cut a straight line in each circle from the outside to the centre. Fit the two circles together with the slits lined up then rotate slightly. This is your angle-maker!

Measure the size of the smaller angle using a protractor. Calculate the size of the other angle. Write the pair of angles.
Repeat for different angles by rotating the circles to new positions.

Name ....

Measuring angles in triangles **for 2 children**

You need a ruler and protractor each, and lots of plain paper.
Work together to draw as many different triangles as you can – scalene, equilateral, isosceles and right-angled. Measure the angles in each triangle you draw, and write the angle sizes inside each one. Write the type of angle next to each one.

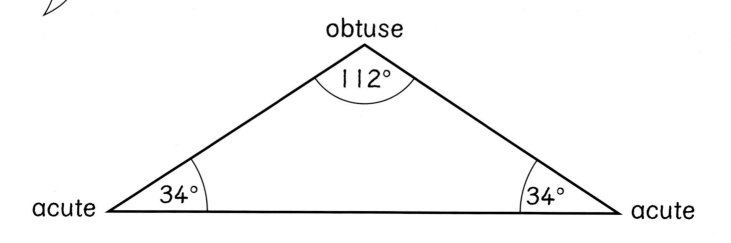

Name

Acute and obtuse

for 2 children

Decide which of you is going to be 'acute' and which is going to be 'obtuse'. One of you draws a straight line, then the other draws another line from the centre, to create one acute angle and one obtuse angle. The 'acute' person estimates the acute angle in degrees. The 'obtuse' person estimates the obtuse angle in degrees. Together, measure the acute angle with a protractor, and then calculate the obtuse angle. Each of you scores points to match the difference between your estimate and the actual size of your angle.

Do this 10 times, swapping roles each time. The winner is the one who scores fewest points!

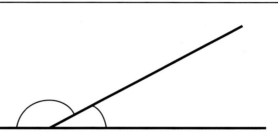

Abacus Evolve Framework Edition Year 5 PCM © Harcourt Education Ltd 2007

Name

Angles within right angles

for 2 children

You need a ruler, a protractor, and several right angles drawn on a sheet of paper.

Choose one of the right angles. One of you draws a line, with a ruler, to divide the angle into two parts. The other person looks at the two angles, and estimates their sizes in degrees. Record the estimates. Remember that the two angles must add up to 90°!

Measure one of the angles each, using a protractor. Write their actual sizes in degrees. Do they add up to 90°?

Repeat this activity several times.

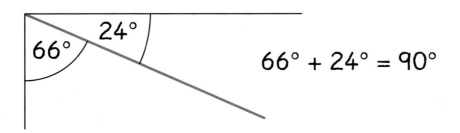

$$66° + 24° = 90°$$

Abacus Evolve Framework Edition Year 5 PCM © Harcourt Education Ltd 2007

Circle polygons

for 3 children

You need several circles drawn on a sheet of paper. Each circle should have six equally spaced marks around the edge (use PCM 183).
Start with one circle, and join some of the points on the circumference to make a polygon. Look at the angles in the shape. How many are acute and how many are obtuse?
Repeat this activity many times, taking turns to draw the polygon.
Can you find any rules to do with the numbers of each type of angle when you join different numbers of points?

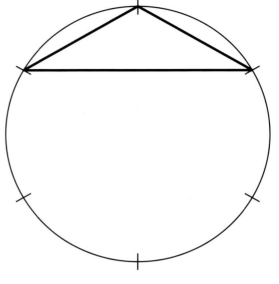

2 acute angles
I obtuse angle

Pentagon angles

for 2 children

You need squared paper.
You are going to draw different pentagons on the squared paper. The angles of the pentagons can be acute, right-angled, obtuse or reflex. Use a ruler!
Draw one pentagon with all five angles obtuse.
Draw one with one right angle and four obtuse angles.
Investigate and draw other combinations of five angles to create different pentagons.

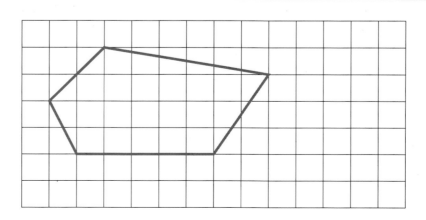

Abacus Evolve Framework Edition Year 5 PCM © Harcourt Education Ltd 2007

Dividing by 3, 4, 6 and 8   **for 2 children**

You need number cards 30–80.
One of you must write down all the multiples of 3 and all the multiples of 6, up to 80. The other must write the multiples of 4 and of 8.
Shuffle the cards and place them face down in a pile. Turn over one card. One of you divides the card number by 3, and then by 6. The other divides the card number by 4, and then by 8. Use your multiple lists to help you. Write down your two answers and the remainders. Discuss the remainders. Take another card and repeat the activity. What do you notice?

$$43$$

$$43 \div 3 = 14 \text{ r } 1$$
$$43 \div 6 = 7 \text{ r } 1$$

$$43 \div 4 = 10 \text{ r } 3$$
$$43 \div 8 = 5 \text{ r } 3$$

Abacus Evolve Framework Edition Year 5 PCM © Harcourt Education Ltd 2007

Division game   **for 6 children**

You need hundreds, tens and units place-value cards, and number cards 2–7. Shuffle the place-value cards and deal one from each set to create a 3-digit number. Shuffle the number cards and deal one to each person. This is their divisor. Each player divides the 3-digit number by their own divisor. Check each other's answers. If your answer is exact, with no remainders, score 10 points. Otherwise, score points to match your remainder.
Play several rounds, reshuffling both sets of cards each time.

$$\boxed{5 \; 2 \; 6} \div \boxed{3} = 175 \text{ r } 1 \qquad \text{score: 1 point}$$

Name ....

Dividing by 9

for 2 or 3 children

Divide 100 by 9.
Divide 200 by 9.
Divide 300 by 9.
Divide 400 by 9.
Divide 500 by 9.
Divide 600 by 9.
Divide 700 by 9.
Divide 800 by 9.
Divide 900 by 9.
Do you notice any patterns? Describe them.

$$9\overline{)100}$$
$$\underline{\quad 90} \qquad 10 \times 9$$
$$\underline{\quad 10}$$

Name ....

Remainder patterns

for 2 children

You need number cards 0–9.
Shuffle the cards. Select three cards, and use them to create a 3-digit number. Work together to divide this number by 2, 3, 4, 5, 6, 7, 8 and 9. Record each answer and its remainder.
Can you see a pattern in the remainders?
Replace the cards and create a new 3-digit number. Repeat the activity.
What do you notice?

$$\boxed{3} \quad \boxed{5} \quad \boxed{8}$$

$$
\begin{array}{r}
179 \\
2\overline{)358} \\
-\ 200 \qquad 100 \times 2 \\
\hline
158 \\
-\ 150 \qquad 75 \times 2 \\
\hline
8 \\
-\quad 8 \qquad 4 \times 2 \\
\hline
0 \qquad 179 \times 2
\end{array}
$$

$$
\begin{array}{r}
119\ r\ 1 \\
3\overline{)358} \\
-\ 300 \qquad 100 \times 3 \\
\hline
58 \\
-\quad 30 \qquad 10 \times 3 \\
\hline
28 \\
-\quad 27 \qquad 9 \times 3 \\
\hline
1 \qquad 119 \times 3
\end{array}
$$

Abacus Evolve Framework Edition Year 5 PCM © Harcourt Education Ltd 2007

Name _____

Ordering mixed numbers

for 2 children

	units	tenths	hundredths
1st number			
2nd number			

You need number cards 0–9.
Shuffle the cards and place them face down in a pile.
Draw a place value grid like this:

Take three cards each. Use them to create a decimal number with two decimal places on the grid. Write down your decimal number, and then turn it into a mixed number. Write the two mixed numbers as an inequality, using the < or > sign.
Replace the cards and repeat the activity. Continue until you have written 10 pairs of numbers.

$$5{\cdot}34 = 5\frac{34}{100} \qquad 2{\cdot}61 = 2\frac{61}{100}$$

$$5\frac{34}{100} > 2\frac{61}{100}$$

Abacus Evolve Framework Edition Year 5 PCM © Harcourt Education Ltd 2007

Name _____

Decimals to mixed numbers

for 3 or 4 children

You need units, tenths and hundredths place-value cards.
Shuffle the cards in their sets, and deal one of each type to each person.
Use your cards to make a decimal number. Take turns to write and say your number as a mixed number. If the others agree that you have said it correctly, score 1 point. You can score an extra 2 points if you can find a simpler equivalent fraction. The others can check your answer.
Play five rounds. Who has scored the most points?

$$\boxed{3 \mid {\cdot}4 \mid 4} = 3\frac{44}{100}$$

$$3\frac{44}{100} = 3\frac{22}{50} = 3\frac{11}{25}$$

Abacus Evolve Framework Edition Year 5 PCM © Harcourt Education Ltd 2007

Name ....

Dice percentages

for 2 or 3 children

Roll a dice 25 times and record the score each time. Write the total number of times each number was thrown. Then work out the percentage of throws that produced each number.

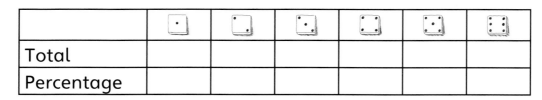

Total						
Percentage						

Repeat, rolling the dice 20 times.

Roll two dice 25 times. For each throw, add the two scores together and record the total. Work out the percentage of throws that produced each total.

Name ....

VAT

for 2 children

VAT stands for Value Added Tax. It is the tax that the government puts on lots of things that we buy. For most items, it is 17·5% of the cost.

VAT = 17·5%

How much VAT would you have to pay for this coat?
What would the price be after VAT is added?
You can work out 17·5% in parts: 10%, 5% and 2·5%.

£64

10%	10% of £64	= £6·40
5% = half of 10%	half of £6·40	= £3·20
2·5% = half of 5%	half of £3·20	= £1·60
Add the three parts together:	£6·40 + £3·20 + £1·60	= £8·20

VAT = £8·20
Price including
VAT = £64 + £8·20 = £72·20

Use this method to find VAT on different prices. Think of at least six different articles of clothing, and a realistic price for each. Find the VAT for each one.

Abacus Evolve Framework Edition Year 5 PCM © Harcourt Education Ltd 2007

Abacus Evolve Framework Edition Year 5 PCM © Harcourt Education Ltd 2007

Squares in a square

for 2 or 3 children

You need squared paper and scissors.
Cut out different sized squares from the squared paper, with sides up to 10 units long. Write the number of small squares inside each.
Extend to squares with sides between 10 and 20 units.

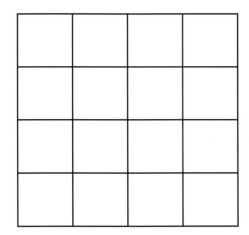

16 squares

Abacus Evolve Framework Edition Year 5 PCM © Harcourt Education Ltd 2007

Digital roots of square numbers

for 2 children

Work together to write a list of all the square numbers from 1^2 to 15^2.
Work out the digital root of each square number (add the digits and keep adding until you reach a single-digit number).
Can you see any patterns in the digital roots?

$7^2 = 49$

digital root of 49: $4 + 9 = 13$ $1 + 3 = 4$

Continue to investigate the digital roots of larger square numbers, for example 20^2, 25^2, 30^2, 35^2 ...

Factor rectangles

for 2 children

You need squared paper and crayons or colouring pencils.
Draw all the possible factor rectangles for these numbers: 12, 24, 36, 48 and 60. Draw the rectangles by colouring squares on the squared paper.
Make sure each rectangle contains the correct number of squares – if you are looking for factor rectangles for the number 12, each rectangle must have 12 squares!

Count how many rectangles you have drawn for each number. Record the numbers of rectangles.

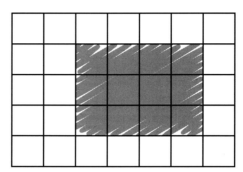

factor rectangle for 12: 3 × 4

List of factors

for 4 children

Work in two pairs to draw tables to show lists of factors of different numbers. One pair will work on the numbers from 20 to 40, the other will work on the numbers from 40 to 60. Start off like this:

20	1, 2, 4, 5, 10, 20
21	1, 3, 7, 21
22	

40	1, 2, 4, 5, 8, 10, 20, 40
41	1, 41
42	

Check each other's lists, then put them together.
Repeat the activity for the factors of numbers 60 to 80 and 80 to 100.
Discuss which numbers have lots of factors, and which have only a few.

Abacus Evolve Framework Edition Year 5 PCM © Harcourt Education Ltd 2007

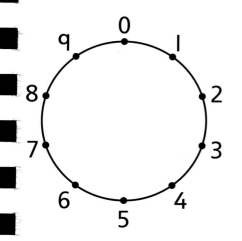
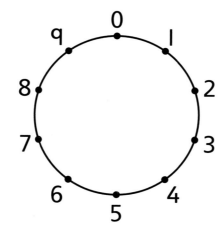
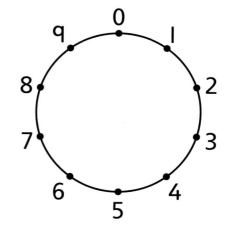

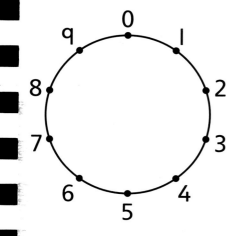
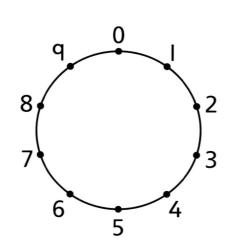
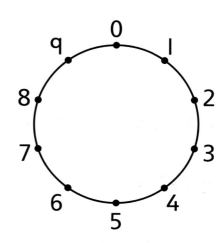

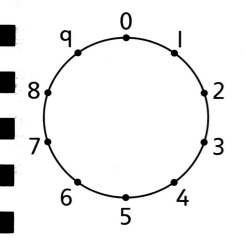
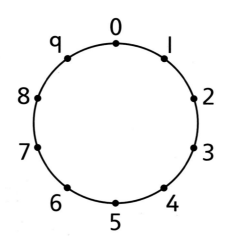
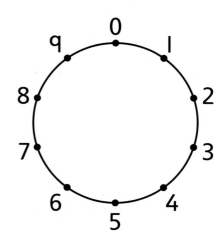

Name

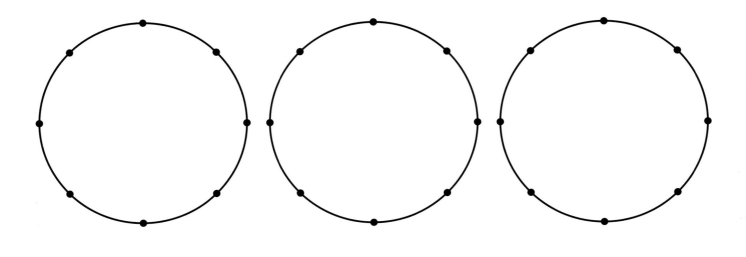

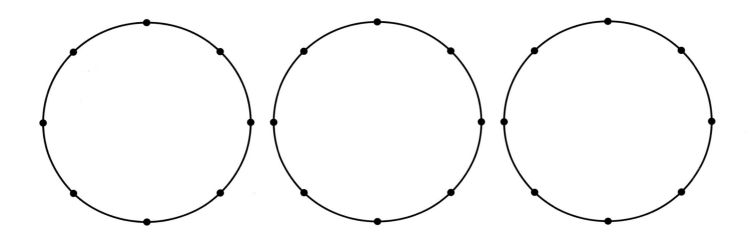

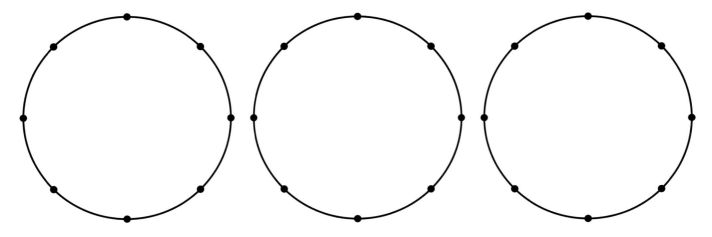

Abacus Evolve Framework Edition Year 5 PCM © Harcourt Education Ltd 2007

Name

Abacus Evolve Framework Edition Year 5 PCM © Harcourt Education Ltd 2007

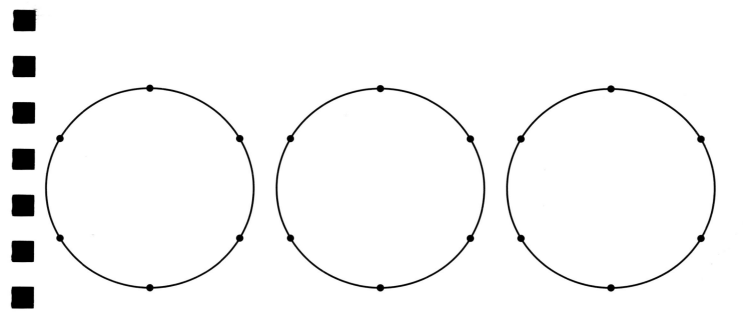

Name _____

$\dfrac{1}{8}$	$\dfrac{1}{6}$	$\dfrac{1}{4}$	$\dfrac{3}{8}$
$\dfrac{1}{3}$	$\dfrac{1}{2}$	$\dfrac{5}{8}$	$\dfrac{2}{3}$
$\dfrac{3}{4}$	$\dfrac{5}{6}$	$\dfrac{7}{8}$	

Abacus Evolve Framework Edition Year 5 PCM © Harcourt Education Ltd 2007

RS

Name

Abacus Evolve Framework Edition Year 5 PCM © Harcourt Education Ltd 2007

Name _____

Abacus Evolve Framework Edition Year 5 PCM © Harcourt Education Ltd 2007

Name

Abacus Evolve Framework Edition Year 5 PCM © Harcourt Education Ltd 2007

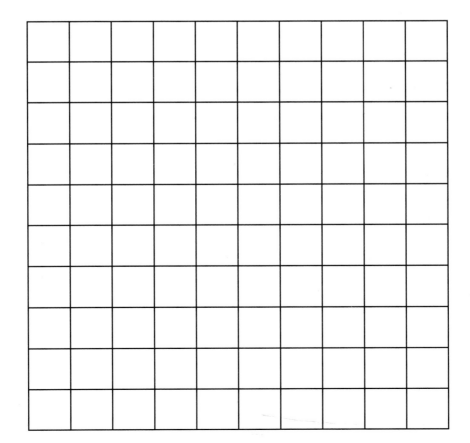

RS

Name ....

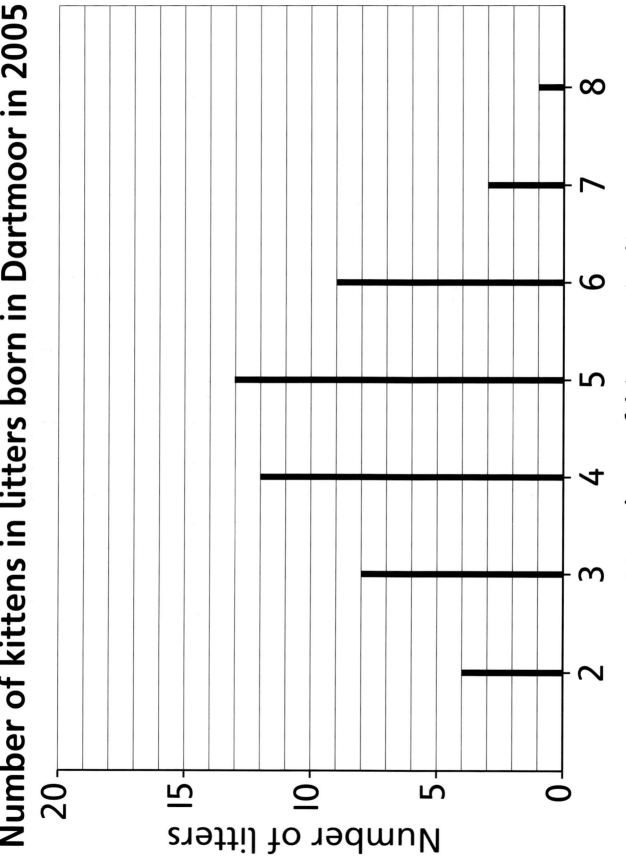

Number of kittens in litters born in Dartmoor in 2005

Number of kittens in litter

Number of litters

Abacus Evolve Framework Edition Year 5 PCM © Harcourt Education Ltd 2007

RS

Name _____

Abacus Evolve Framework Edition Year 5 PCM © Harcourt Education Ltd 2007

Number of kittens in litters born in Dartmoor in 2005

Number of kittens in litter	Frequency
2	4
3	8
4	12
5	13
6	9
7	3
8	1

RS

Name ....

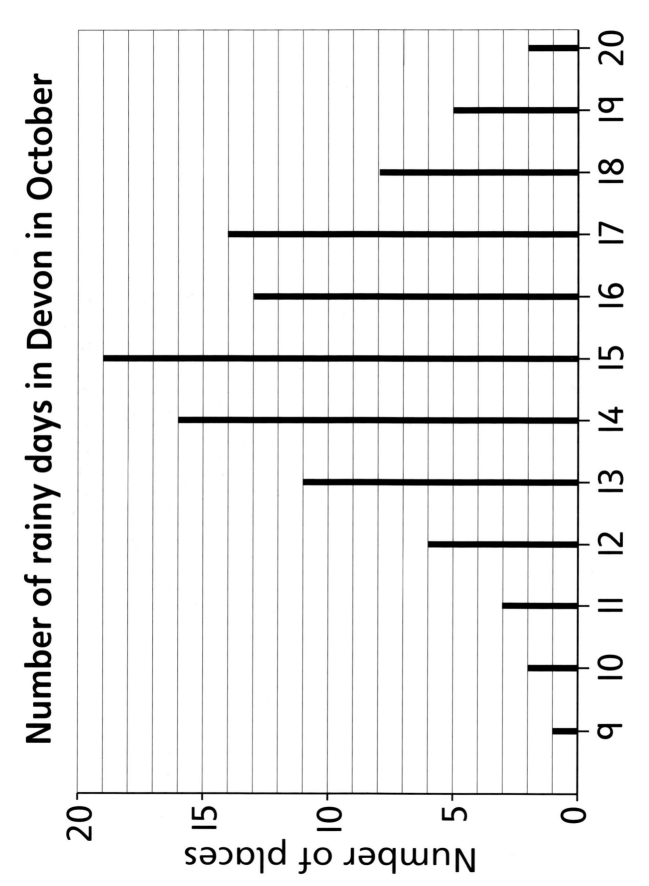

Number of rainy days in Devon in October

Number of rainy days

Number of places

Abacus Evolve Framework Edition Year 5 PCM © Harcourt Education Ltd 2007

Name ....

Abacus Evolve Framework Edition Year 5 PCM © Harcourt Education Ltd 2007

Number of rainy days in northern Spain in October

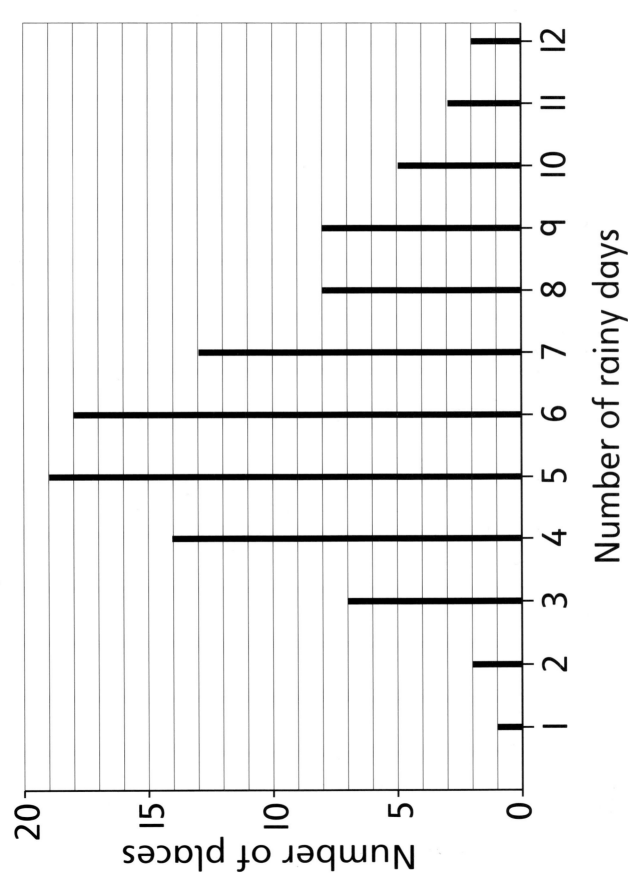

Number of rainy days

Number of places

Name ....

Number of sunny days in English cities in one week in August

City	Number of sunny days in one week	City	Number of sunny days in one week
Bath	6	Leicester	4
Birmingham	5	Lincoln	4
Bradford	3	Liverpool	3
Brighton and Hove	7	London	5
Bristol	6	Manchester	3
Cambridge	5	Newcastle	1
Canterbury	6	Norwich	4
Carlisle	1	Nottingham	4
Chester	3	Oxford	5
Durham	1	Portsmouth	7
Exeter	6	Sheffield	3
Gloucester	5	Southampton	7
Hull	2	Stratford-upon-Avon	5
Lancaster	2	Winchester	6
Leeds	2	York	2

RS

Name _____

Abacus Evolve Framework Edition Year 5 PCM © Harcourt Education Ltd 2007

Number of sunny days in Scottish towns and cities in one week in August

City/town	Number of sunny days in one week	City/town	Number of sunny days in one week
Aberdeen	1	Inverness	1
Alyth	3	Kilmarnock	4
Blairgowrie	3	Kinross	3
Carnoustie	3	Montrose	2
Dumfries	5	Perth	3
Dundee	2	Peterhead	1
Dunfermline	3	Prestwick	4
Durness	0	Renfrew	4
Edinburgh	4	Roslin	4
Elgin	1	Rothesay	3
Falkirk	3	Selkirk	4
Glasgow	4	Stirling	3
Helensburgh	3	Strathaven	4
Inverbervie	2	Whithorn	5
Invergordon	1	Wick	0

RS

Name _____

Temperature of tea in an ordinary mug

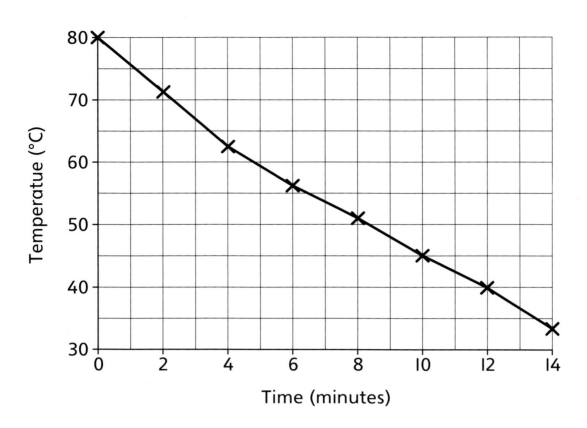

Temperature of tea in a vacuum-insulated mug

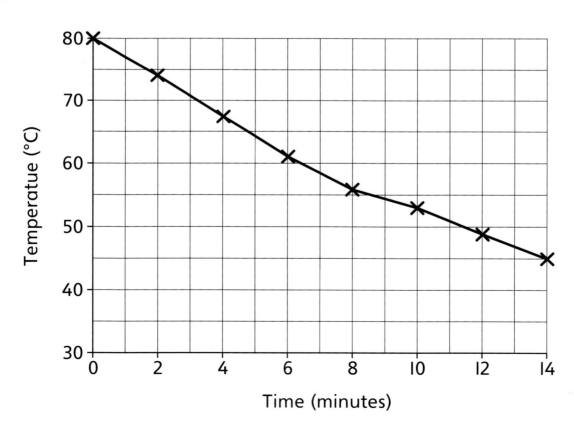

Abacus Evolve Framework Edition Year 5 PCM © Harcourt Education Ltd 2007

Name ....

Noise level in a classroom during a lesson

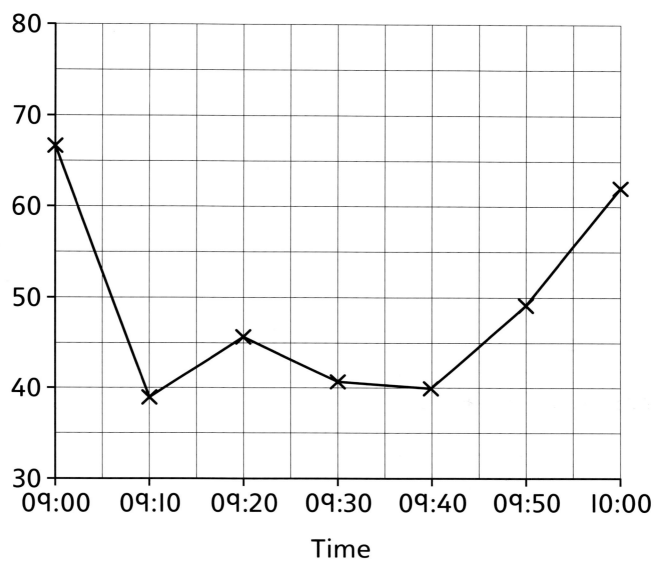

Abacus Evolve Framework Edition Year 5 PCM © Harcourt Education Ltd 2007

Noon temperatures in the first two weeks of January

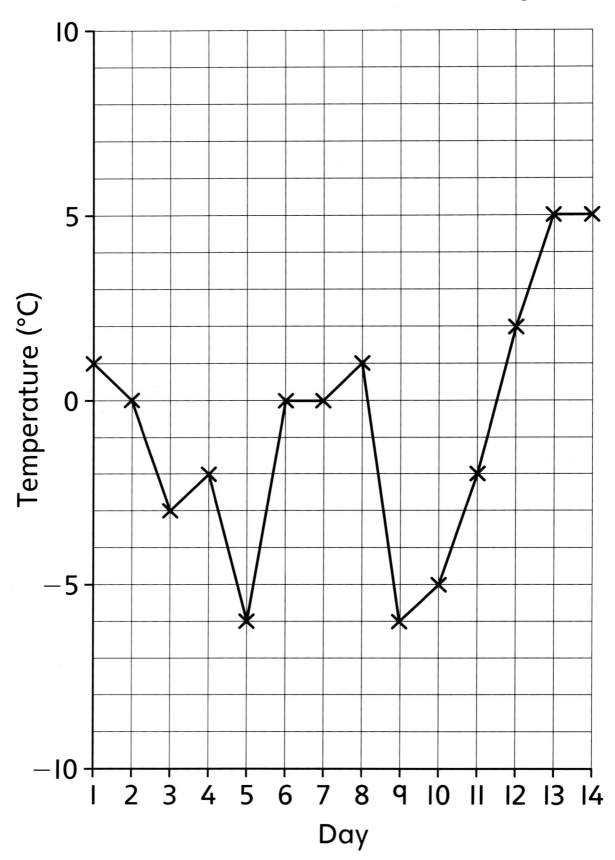

Abacus Evolve Framework Edition Year 5 PCM © Harcourt Education Ltd 2007

Size of a melting ice cube

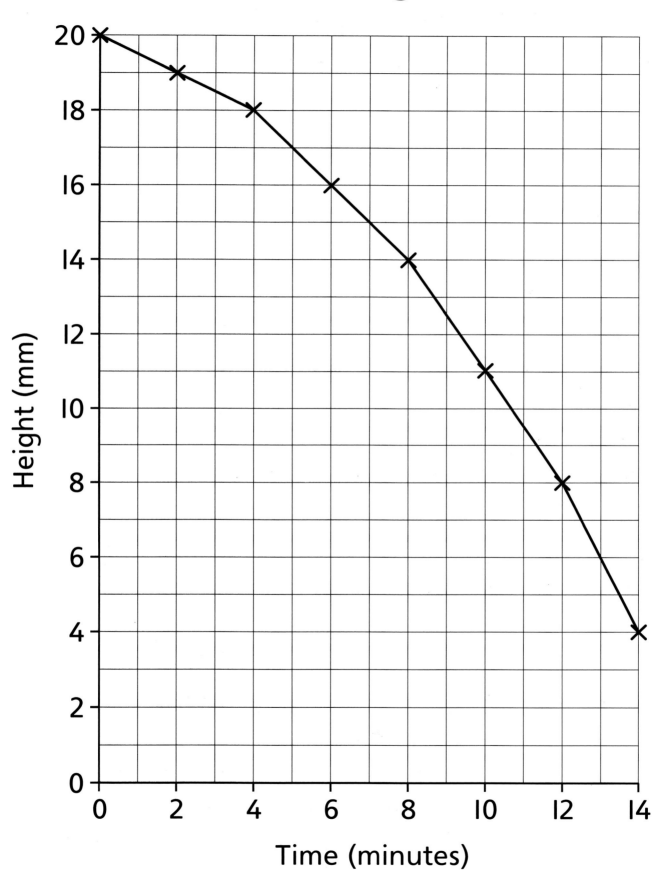

Name

12 times table line graph

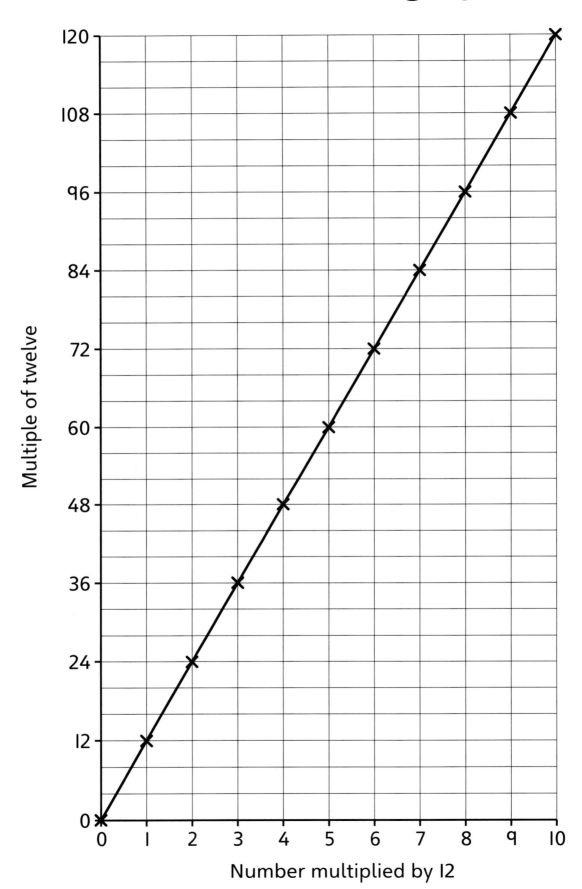

Multiple of twelve

Number multiplied by 12

Abacus Evolve Framework Edition Year 5 PCM © Harcourt Education Ltd 2007

Name _____

Abacus Evolve Framework Edition Year 5 PCM © Harcourt Education Ltd 2007

Name _____

Abacus Evolve Framework Edition Year 5 PCM © Harcourt Education Ltd 2007

Name

Abacus Evolve Framework Edition Year 5 PCM © Harcourt Education Ltd 2007

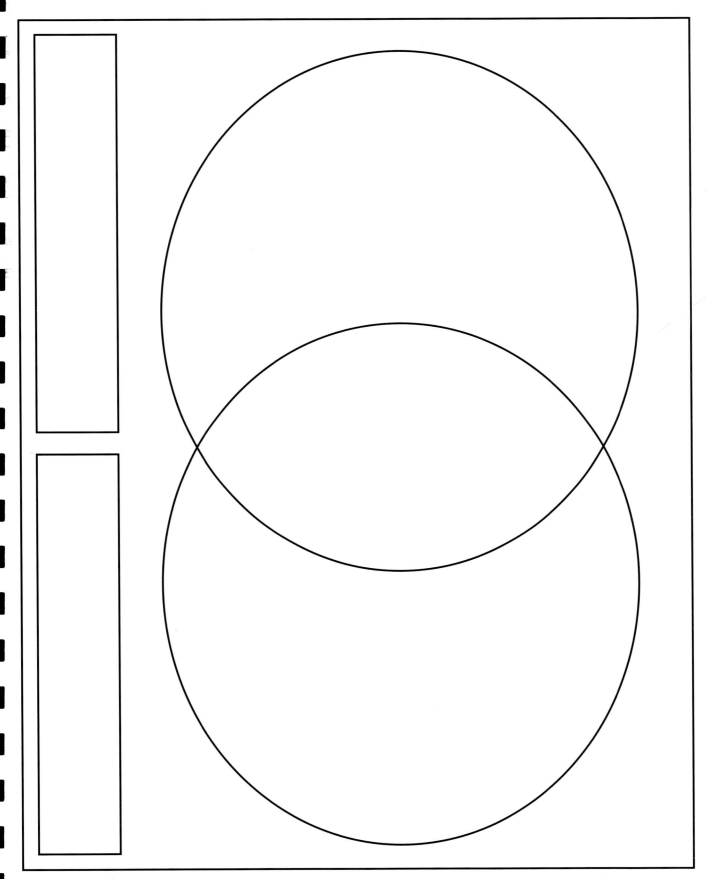

Name

Abacus Evolve Framework Edition Year 5 PCM © Harcourt Education Ltd 2007

T (thousands)	H (hundreds)	T (tens)	U (units)

RS

Name _____

Abacus Evolve Framework Edition Year 5 PCM © Harcourt Education Ltd 2007

100Th (hundred thousands)	10Th (ten thousands)	Th (thousands)	H (hundreds)	T (tens)	U (units)

Abacus Evolve Framework Edition Year 5 PCM © Harcourt Education Ltd 2007

T (tens)	**U** (units)	**t** (tenths)	**h** (hundredths)

RS

Name

Abacus Evolve Framework Edition Year 5 PCM © Harcourt Education Ltd 2007

1	2	3	4	5	6	7	8	9	10
11	12	13	14	15	16	17	18	19	20
21	22	23	24	25	26	27	28	29	30
31	32	33	34	35	36	37	38	39	40
41	42	43	44	45	46	47	48	49	50
51	52	53	54	55	56	57	58	59	60
61	62	63	64	65	66	67	68	69	70
71	72	73	74	75	76	77	78	79	80
81	82	83	84	85	86	87	88	89	90
91	92	93	94	95	96	97	98	99	100

RS

Name _____

91	92	93	94	95	96	97	98	99	100
81	82	83	84	85	86	87	88	89	90
71	72	73	74	75	76	77	78	79	80
61	62	63	64	65	66	67	68	69	70
51	52	53	54	55	56	57	58	59	60
41	42	43	44	45	46	47	48	49	50
31	32	33	34	35	36	37	38	39	40
21	22	23	24	25	26	27	28	29	30
11	12	13	14	15	16	17	18	19	20
1	2	3	4	5	6	7	8	9	10

Abacus Evolve Framework Edition Year 5 PCM © Harcourt Education Ltd 2007

Name ....

Abacus Evolve Framework Edition Year 5 PCM © Harcourt Education Ltd 2007

1	2	3	4	5	6	7	8	9	10
2	4	6	8	10	12	14	16	18	20
3	6	9	12	15	18	21	24	27	30
4	8	12	16	20	24	28	32	36	40
5	10	15	20	25	30	35	40	45	50
6	12	18	24	30	36	42	48	54	60
7	14	21	28	35	42	49	56	63	70
8	16	24	32	40	48	56	64	72	80
9	18	27	36	45	54	63	72	81	90
10	20	30	40	50	60	70	80	90	100

RS

Name

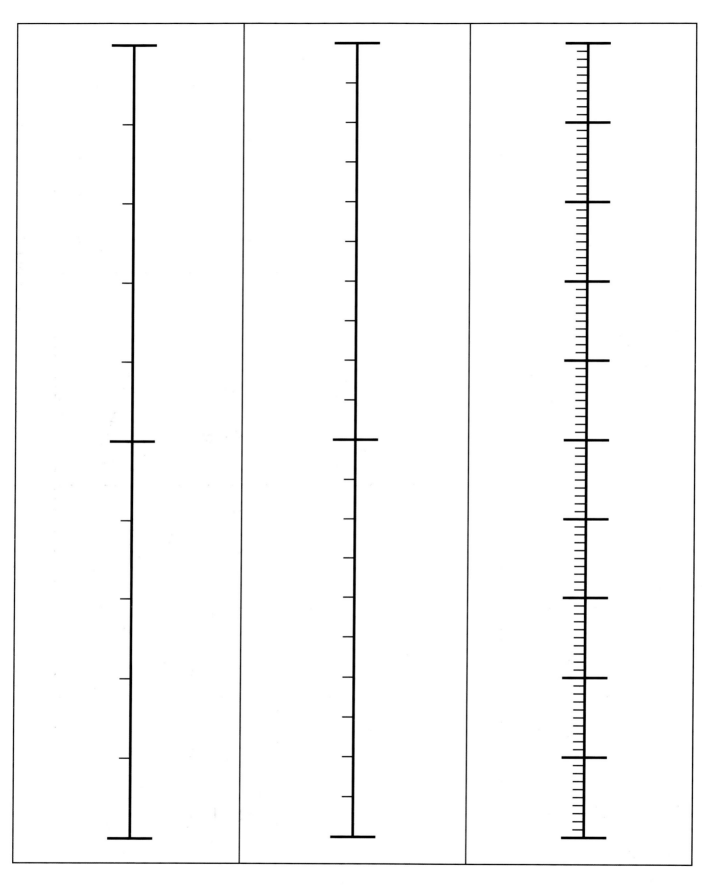

Abacus Evolve Framework Edition Year 5 PCM © Harcourt Education Ltd 2007

RS

Name

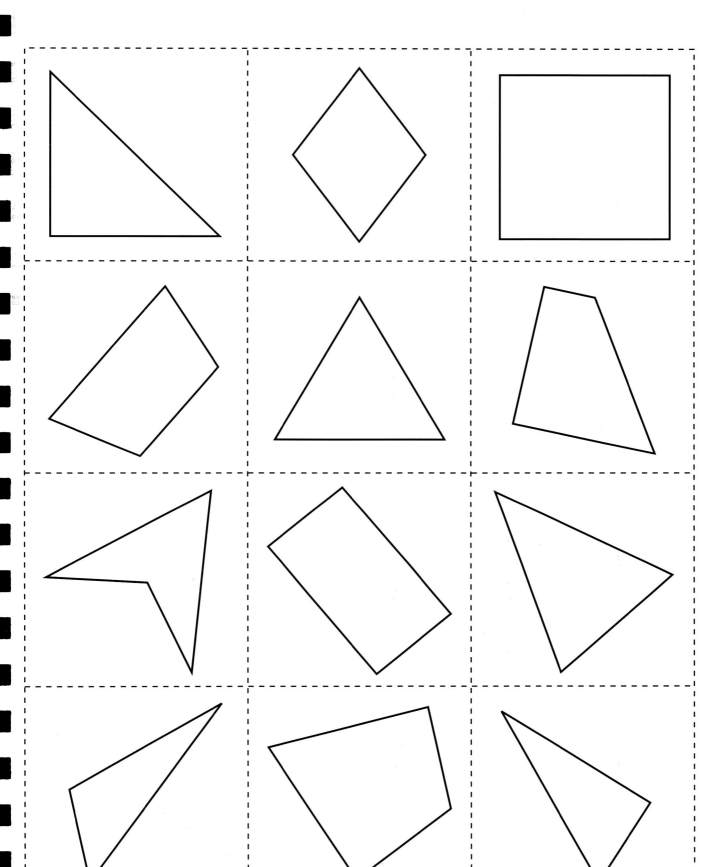

RS

Name

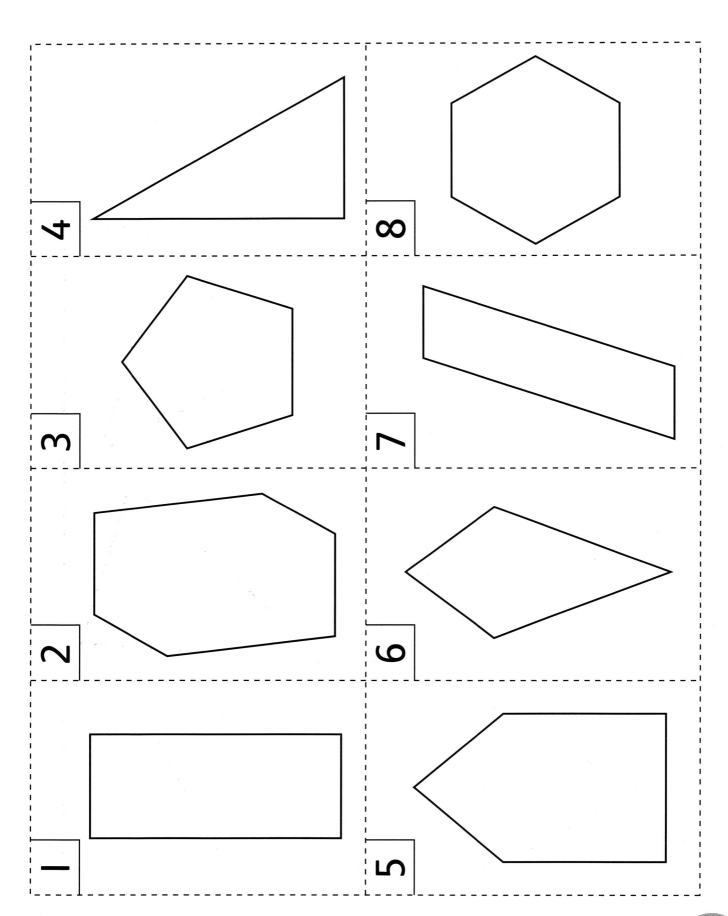

4

8

3

7

2

6

1

5

Abacus Evolve Framework Edition Year 5 PCM © Harcourt Education Ltd 2007

RS

Name

Abacus Evolve Framework Edition Year 5 PCM © Harcourt Education Ltd 2007

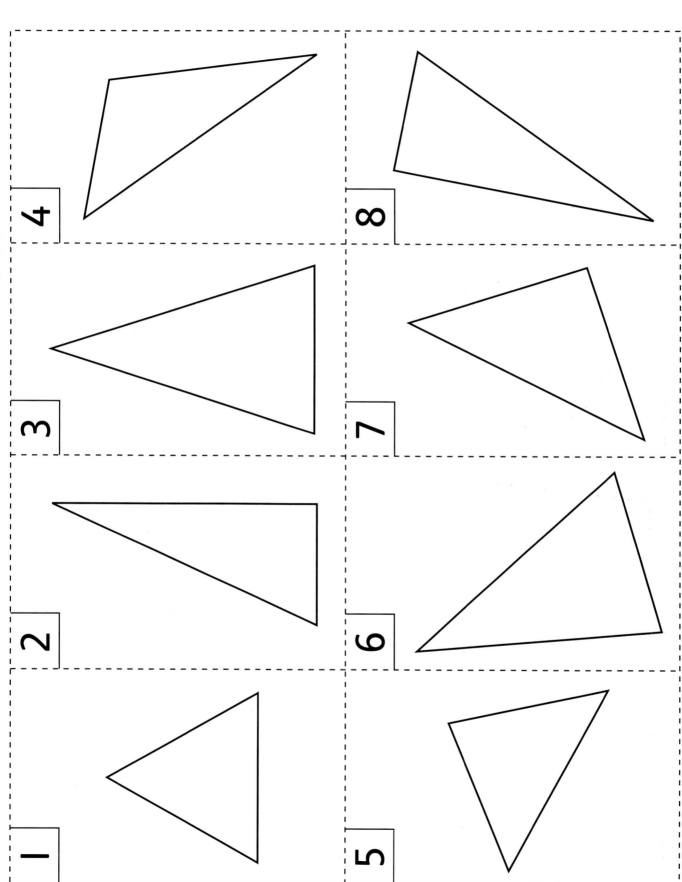

4

8

3

7

2

6

1

5

Name

Abacus Evolve Framework Edition Year 5 PCM © Harcourt Education Ltd 2007

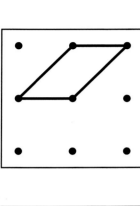
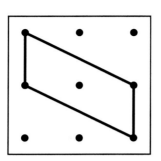
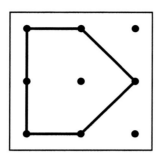
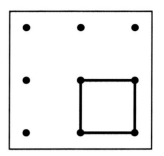
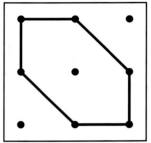
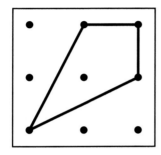
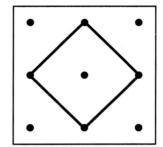
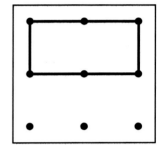
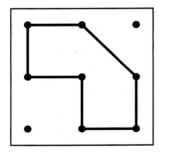
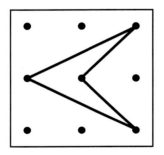
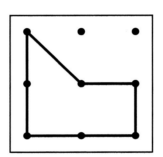
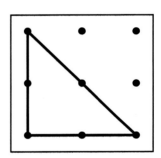
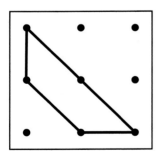
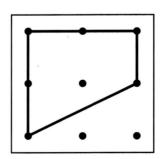
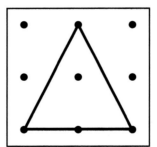
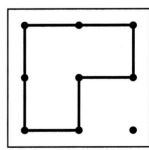

Name

Abacus Evolve Framework Edition Year 5 PCM © Harcourt Education Ltd 2007

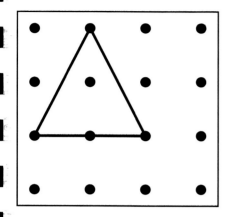
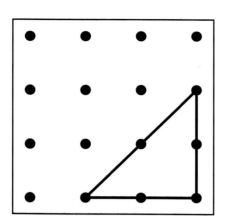
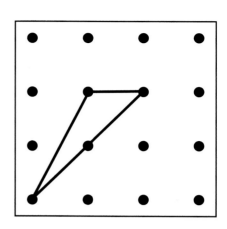

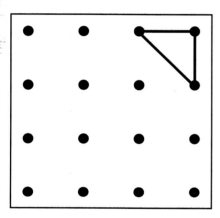
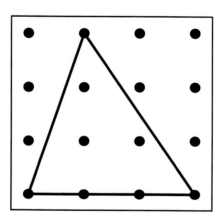
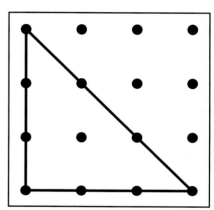

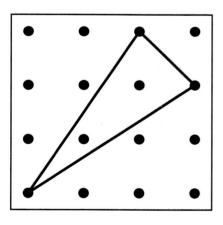
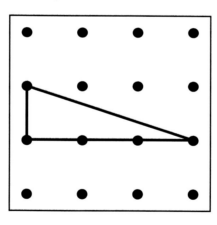
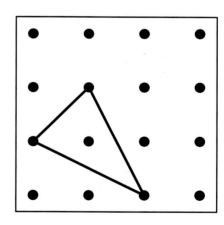

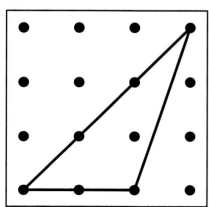
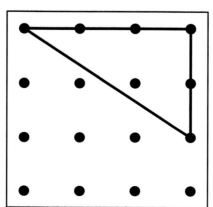
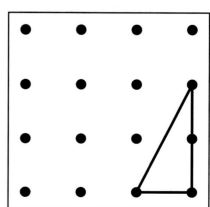

Name

Abacus Evolve Framework Edition Year 5 PCM © Harcourt Education Ltd 2007

Name _____

Abacus Evolve Framework Edition Year 5 PCM © Harcourt Education Ltd 2007

Name

Abacus Evolve Framework Edition Year 5 PCM © Harcourt Education Ltd 2007

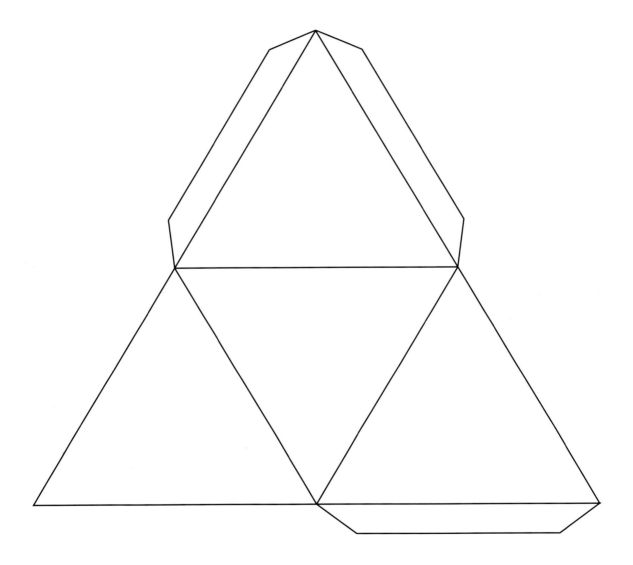

Name

Name _____

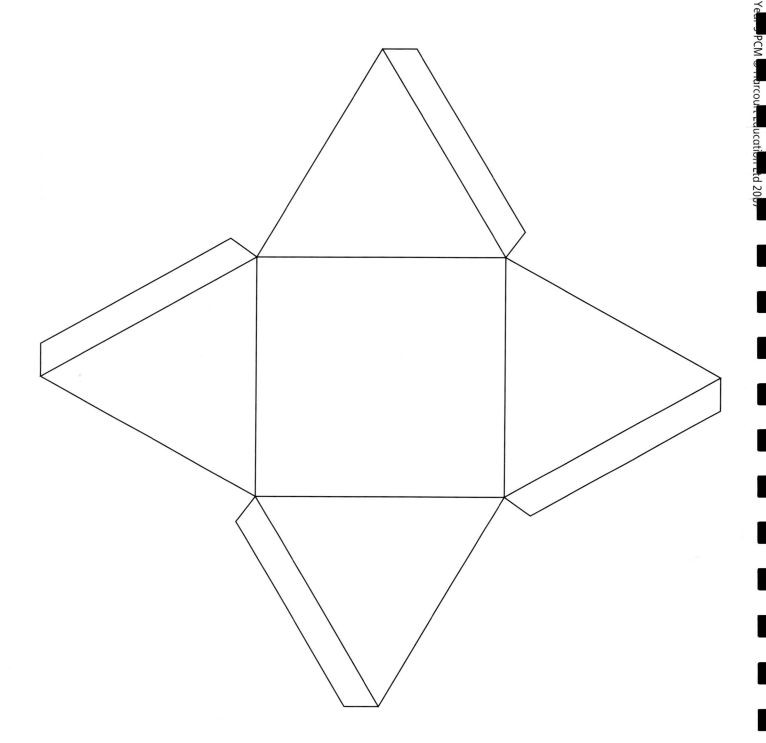

Abacus Evolve Framework Edition Year 5 PCM © Harcourt Education Ltd 2007

Name _____

Name _____

Distances between cities in England

	Birmingham	Dover	Liverpool	Newcastle	Norwich
Dover	207 miles				
Liverpool	93 miles	281 miles			
Newcastle	355 miles	257 miles	155 miles		
Norwich	144 miles	156 miles	220 miles	260 miles	
Plymouth	207 miles	287 miles	283 miles	412 miles	315 miles

RS

Name _____

Round trips

Destination	Distance of round trip
Seaside	26 miles
Forest	34 miles
City centre	28 miles
Theme park	54 miles
Cinema	16 miles
Nature reserve	41 miles
Theatre	37 miles
Sports stadium	45 miles
Farm	19 miles
Aqua park	22 miles

Name _____

Abacus Evolve Framework Edition Year 5 PCM © Harcourt Education Ltd 2007

Chocolate brownies

- 350 g chocolate
- 250 g butter
- 250 g dark sugar
- 100 g plain flour
- 3 eggs
- 5 g baking powder

Fruit cake

- 500 g dried fruit
- 350 g brown sugar
- 300 g raisins
- 300 g white flour
- 170 g butter
- 60 g treacle
- 4 eggs
- 15 g cinnamon
- 10 g baking powder
- 10 g salt
- 5 g nutmeg

Chocolate chip cookies

- 350 g flour
- 350 g choc chips
- 225 g butter
- 175 g caster sugar
- 175 g brown sugar
- 2 eggs
- 5 g baking soda
- 5 g salt
- 5 ml vanilla essence

Wholemeal bread

- 450 g wholemeal flour
- 300 ml water
- 15 g yeast
- 8 g butter
- 5 g salt
- 5 g brown sugar

RS

Name

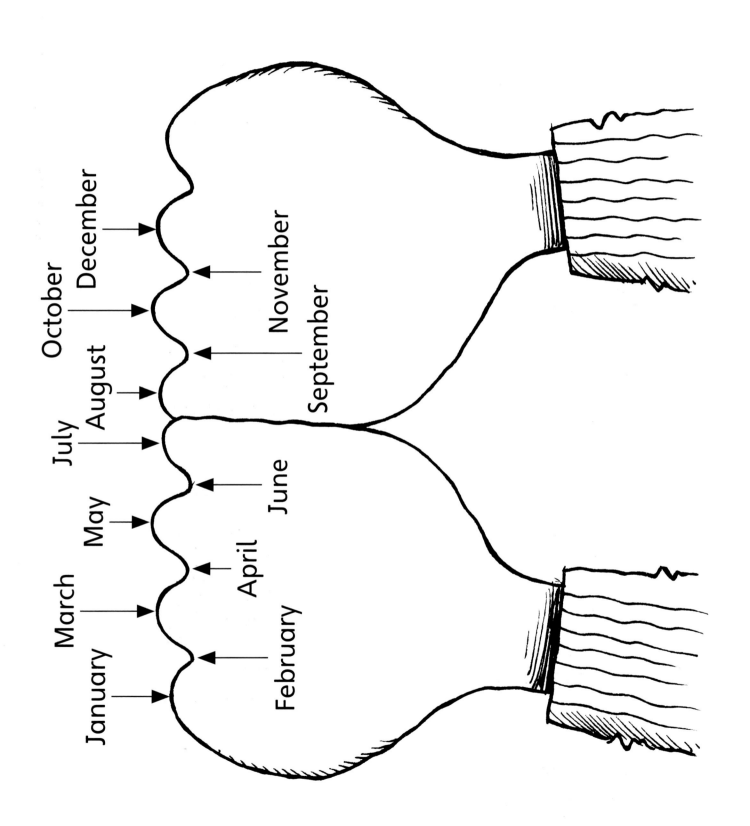

October December November September

July August June

March May April February

January

Abacus Evolve Framework Edition Year 5 PCM © Harcourt Education Ltd 2007

Name _____

sundial

sand clock

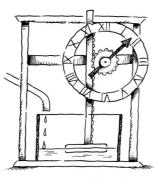

water clock

candle clock

pendulum clock

spring clock
(bracket clock)

digital clock

Name _____

Abacus Evolve Framework Edition Year 5 PCM © Harcourt Education Ltd 2007

Train timetables

London to Paris

London	Ashford	Calais	Lille	Paris
06:34	07:24	07:56	–	09:23
07:09	07:59	–	08:56	09:59
07:39	08:29	–	–	10:23
08:12	–	–	–	10:47
09:09	09:59	–	-	11:53
11:40	–	–	13:21	14:23
12:09	12:59	13:31	–	14:59
13:41	–	–	15:21	16:23
17:09	17:59	18:31	–	19:59
18:42	–	–	–	21:23

London to Brussels

London	Ashford	Calais	Lille	Brussels
06:10	06:59	–	07:56	08:37
07:43	–	–	–	09:58
08:39	09:30	–	10:26	11:08
10:43	–	–	12:24	12:05
12:41	13:30	–	14:29	15:10
14:42	–	–	16:21	17:02
16:39	17:29	–	18:29	19:10
18:11	–	–	19:56	20:37

Note: times are according to GMT

RS

Name _____

Abacus Evolve Framework Edition Year 5 PCM © Harcourt Education Ltd 2007

1930 ship timetable

Southampton	Gibraltar	Port Said	Aden	Mombassa	Dar es Salaam	Durban	Cape Town
11th May	13th May	17th May	19th May	21st May	22nd May	24th May	25th May

2006 flight timetable

London	Cape Town
11th May 19:35	12th May 06:05

Note: times are according to GMT

Queensford Cinema
30th June, 1930

6.00 pm   National anthem
6.05 pm   News
6.15 pm   "Dawn Chorus" – comedy interest film
6.25 pm   "Charlie's Cat" – colour cartoon
6.30 pm   *Interval*
6.40 pm   "Journey to Arabia" – main feature (79 minutes)

Queensford Cinema
30th June, 2006

Pet Patrol (107 minutes)	18:00	20:15
Shark Shock (96 mins)	18:20	20:25
Bruce Force (125 mins)	18:35	20:55
Shooting Stars (98 mins)	19:15	21:10
Fire! (118 mins)	19:30	21:45

QUEENSFORD CINEMA
30TH JUNE, 2020

Hover Rider's Revenge (43 mins)	09:30
There's An Alien Under My Bed! (35 mins)	11:45
Mumba's Mars Mission (57 mins)	13:05
Jackball Fever (49 mins)	15:20
My Pet Firebadger (32 mins)	17:35
Space Wars 7 (58 mins)	19:00
Spliced (45 mins)	21:15
Killer Clones (51 mins)	23:50

RS

Name ....

Abacus Evolve Framework Edition Year 5 PCM © Harcourt Education Ltd 2007

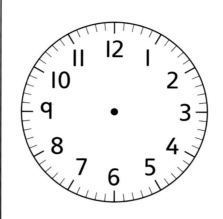

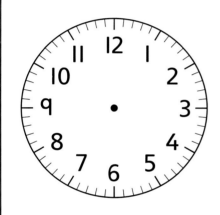

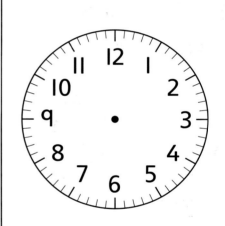

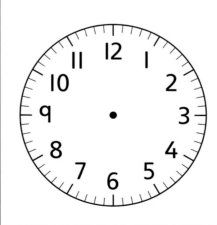

Name ....

World temperatures, December

Athens, Greece	19°C	New Delhi, India	23°C
Beijing, China	9°C	New York, USA	2°C
Cairo, Egypt	25°C	Paris, France	3°C
Cape Town, S. Africa	29°C	Rio de Janeiro, Brazil	31°C
Helsinki, Finland	⁻1°C	Rome, Italy	10°C
Istanbul, Turkey	13°C	Seoul, S. Korea	14°C
Lima, Peru	21°C	Tokyo, Japan	18°C
Madrid, Spain	10°C	Toronto, Canada	⁻14°C
Miami, USA	26°C	Warsaw, Poland	0°C
Moscow, Russia	⁻3°C	Wellington, New Zealand	12°C

Abacus Evolve Framework Edition Year 5 PCM © Harcourt Education Ltd 2007

RS

Name

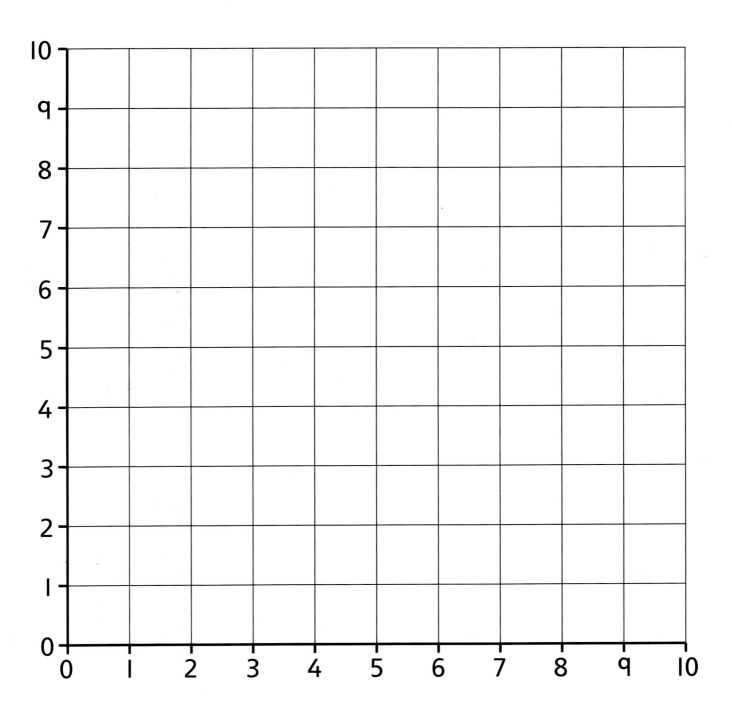

Abacus Evolve Framework London Year 5 PCM © Harcourt Education Ltd 2007

Abacus Evolve Framework Edition Year 5 PCM © Harcourt Education Ltd 2007

unlikely	impossible
certain	likely
even chance	good chance
no chance	poor chance

RS

Name _____

Football league table

	Played	Won	Drew	Lost	Goals for	Goals against	Goal diff.	Points
Tatsfield	18	13	5	0	35	10	25	44
Kellerston	18	12	4	2	31	15	16	40
Bagford	18	10	4	4	18	12	6	34
Wintertown	18	10	0	8	23	21	2	30
Gumpsey	18	9	2	7	29	25	4	29
Trapmouth	18	8	3	7	20	21	-1	27
Anderville	18	7	2	9	17	27	-10	23
Neverley	18	5	5	8	24	32	-8	20
Munston	18	1	2	15	21	40	-19	5
Shingleford	18	0	1	17	11	36	-25	1

RS

Name _____

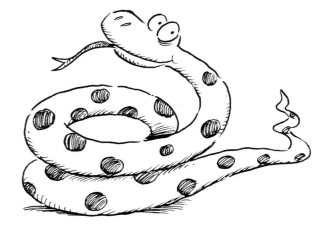

7 litres	1000 litres	50 millilitres
10 millilitres	$1\frac{1}{2}$ litres	175 litres

RS

Name _____

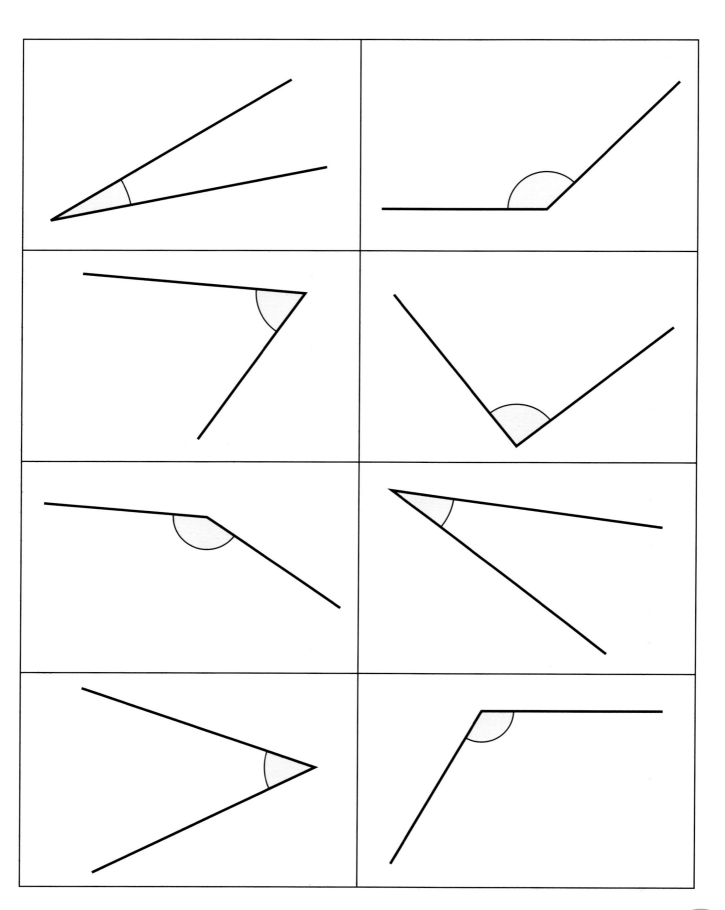

Abacus Evolve Framework Edition Year 5 PCM © Harcourt Education Ltd 2007

RS

Abacus Evolve Framework Edition Year 5 PCM © Harcourt Education Ltd 2007

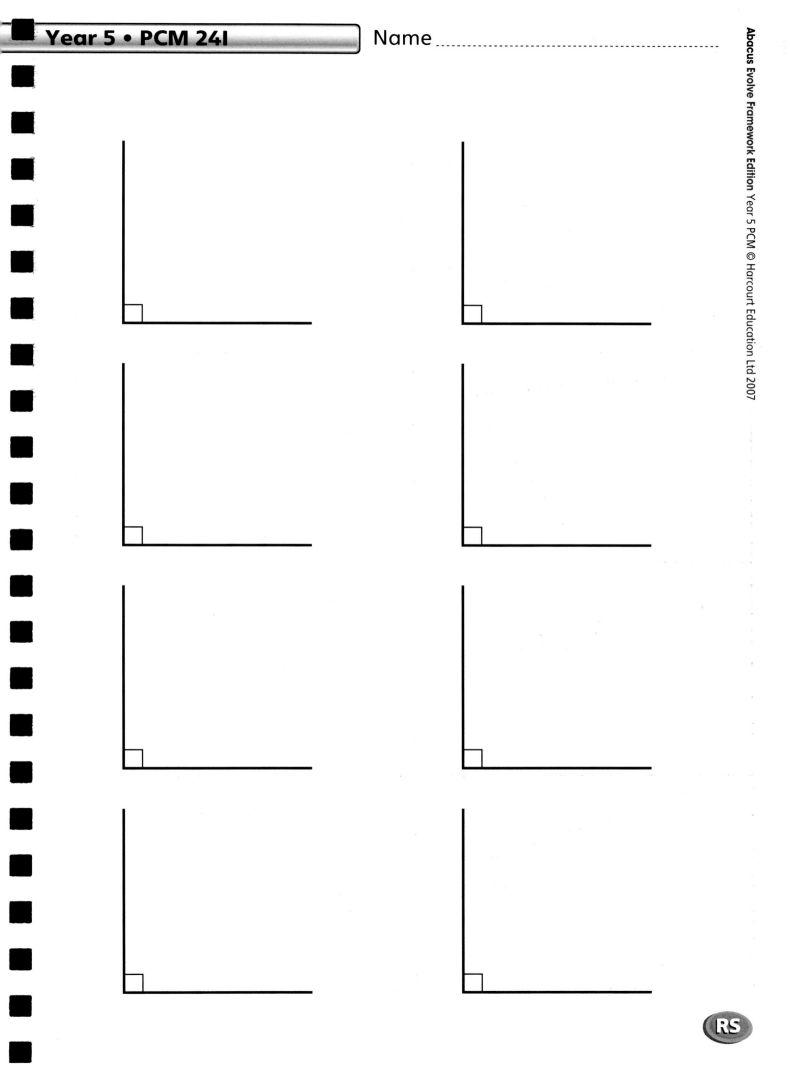

Name _____

Abacus Evolve Framework Edition Year 5 PCM © Harcourt Education Ltd 2007

Name _____

Abacus Evolve Framework Edition Year 5 PCM © Harcourt Education Ltd 2007

Name _____

Abacus Evolve Framework Edition Year 5 PCM © Harcourt Education Ltd 2007

Name _____

Abacus Evolve Framework Edition Year 5 PCM © Harcourt Education Ltd 2007

Distances in Britain mileage chart

	London	Birmingham	Cardiff	Dover	Edinburgh	Liverpool	Manchester	Nottingham	Penzance	Sheffield
Birmingham	177									
Cardiff	155	105								
Dover	76	201	241							
Edinburgh	405	294	394	466						
Liverpool	203	97	198	290	221					
Manchester	197	88	188	274	217	35				
Nottingham	124	55	169	199	268	103	71			
Penzance	282	272	244	366	560	376	360	340		
Sheffield	165	78	205	238	248	74	37	38	363	

RS

Name

Multiplication and division facts

$6 \times 3 =$	$24 \div 3 =$
$5 \times 8 =$	$18 \div 2 =$
$7 \times 4 =$	$24 \div 4 =$
$9 \times 7 =$	$42 \div 6 =$
$8 \times 6 =$	$56 \div 7 =$
$9 \times 5 = 45$	$5 \times 9 = 45$
$45 \div 5 = 9$	$45 \div 9 = 5$

AS

Name ....

Shapes

Abacus Evolve Framework Edition Year 5 PCM © Harcourt Education Ltd 2007

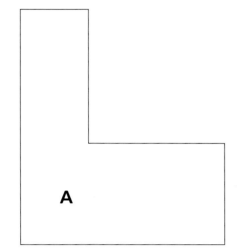

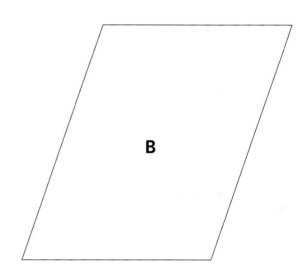

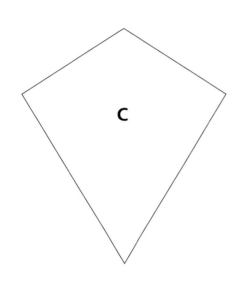

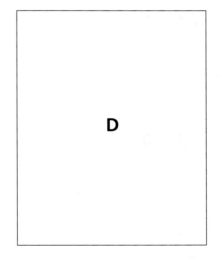

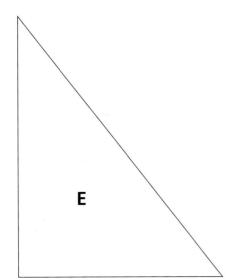

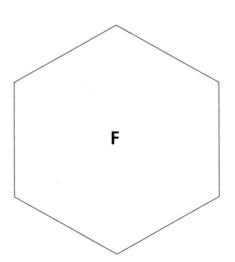

AS

Name ....

Parallel and perpendicular

	Parallel sides	**No parallel sides**
Perpendicular sides		
No perpendicular sides		

AS

Name

Abacus Evolve Framework Edition Year 5 PCM © Harcourt Education Ltd 2007

Metric units

mm	cm	m	km
10	100	1000	
3·45 m	45·78 m	20·67 m	2·09 m
0·85 m	0·04 m	1·965 km	12·835 km
5·034 km	7·002 km	0·870 km	0·035 km

AS

Name ....

Finding differences

Set A

18

48

62

85

100

Set B

72

100

133

165

192

Set C

228

272

291

357

403

Set D

587

644

821

1010

1632

Name _____

Multiplying and dividing by 10 and 100

Abacus Evolve Framework Edition Year 5 PCM © Harcourt Education Ltd 2007

$134 \times 10 = 1340$	$240 \div 10 = 24$
$575 \times 10 = 5705$	$1750 \div 10 = 175$
$766 \times 10 = 776$	$5030 \div 10 = 530$
$528 \times 100 = 52\,800$	$4200 \div 10 = 42$
$306 \times 100 = 30\,600$	$5800 \div 100 = 58$
$907 \times 100 = 90\,070$	$5000 \div 100 = 5$

AS

Name ....

Rounding integers

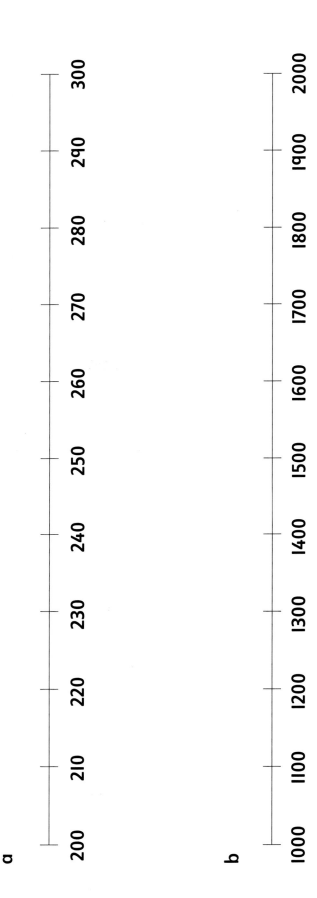

a

300
290
280
270
260
250
240
230
220
210
200

b

2000
1900
1800
1700
1600
1500
1400
1300
1200
1100
1000

c

10000
9000
8000
7000
6000
5000
4000
3000
2000
1000
0

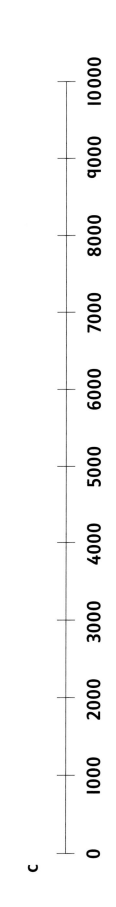

Abacus Evolve Framework Edition Year 5 PCM © Harcourt Education Ltd 2007

AS

Name

Abacus Evolve Framework Edition Year 5 PCM © Harcourt Education Ltd 2007

Area and perimeter of rectangles

4cm | A | 6cm

7cm | B | 5cm

3cm | C

D | 6cm

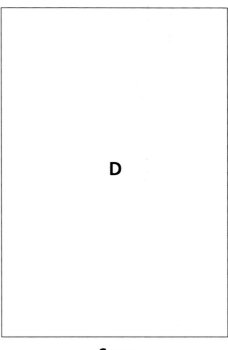

AS

Name ....

Relationship between addition and subtraction

a $9 + 7 + \underline{} = 21$

b $40 + 30 + \underline{} = 120$

c $32 + 64 + \underline{} = 137$

d $52 + \underline{} + 84 = 179$

e $70 + \underline{} + 90 + 30 = 240$

f $15 + 23 + 42 + \underline{} = 137$

Abacus Evolve Framework Edition Year 5 PCM © Harcourt Education Ltd 2007

AS

Abacus Evolve Framework Edition Year 5 PCM © Harcourt Education Ltd 2007

Equivalence of fractions and decimals

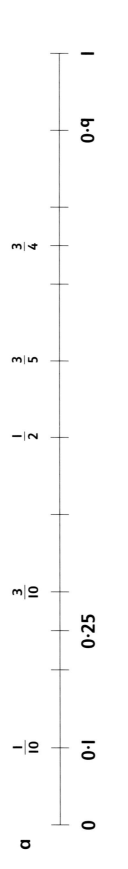

a

$\frac{1}{10}$		$\frac{3}{10}$			$\frac{1}{2}$	$\frac{3}{5}$	$\frac{3}{4}$		1
0	0·1	0·25						0·9	

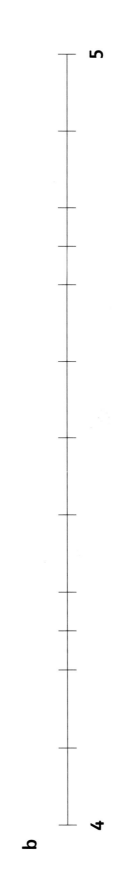

b

4   5

Name _____

Multiplication and division

Multiplication

1   The width of a bookcase is 2·3 metres.
    If three of these bookcases are put beside each other,
    what would be the total width?

2   The weight of a Samsite 3 television is 5·7 kg.
    How much would four televisions weigh?

3   A bucket holds 8·9 litres of water.
    How much water could six similar buckets hold?

Division

1   46 sweets are shared between 3 children.
    How many does each child get and how many are left over?

2   132 cubes are arranged into groups of 5.
    How many cubes in each group?
    How many are left over?

3   Joy bought 272 stickers. They come in packs of 6.
    How many packets has she bought?

Abacus Evolve Framework Edition Year 5 PCM © Harcourt Education Ltd 2007

(AS)

Name ....

Rounding decimals

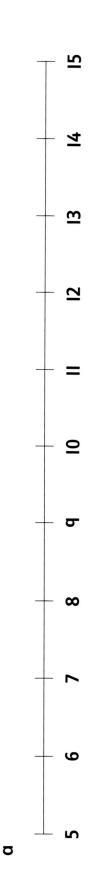

a

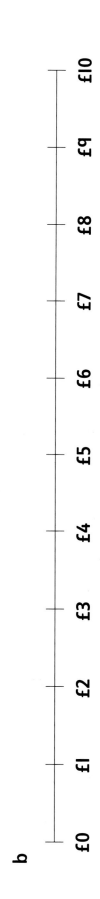

b

Abacus Evolve Framework Edition Year 5 PCM © Harcourt Education Ltd 2007

AS

Name ....

Addition using standard methods

1 587 + 451 = 1138

2 426 + 385 = 811

3 2535 + 3421 = 5846

4 3978 + 4216 = 8194

5 4031 + 1223 + 2324 = 7578

6 4855 + 4561 + 6865 = 15191

Abacus Evolve Framework Edition Year 5 PCM © Harcourt Education Ltd 2007

AS